Christie,
Romans 8:28 assures us that all things work for our good when we trust God. Not only the good, but the bad too are mixed together to create a beautiful life. May you see a glimpse of that as you journey through Grace Maps.
Blessings,
Carmen

Grace Maps

OUR JOURNEY GUIDED BY GOD'S GRACE

CARMEN HORNE

Carmen Horne
Romans 8:28

Grace Maps: Our Journey Guided by God's Grace

www.carmenhorne.com

ISBN: 978-1-7332627-3-6 (Paperback)
Published by Cotton Port Publishing, LLC

Cover and interior design: Typewriter Creative Co.
Author Photo: Misti Mixon Stone

Working through my Grace Map has been such an eye-opening journey for me. As someone who doesn't like to talk about their feelings, it's been so good for my heart to have a guide like this. Carmen's prompts have helped me process through the different seasons of my life, the good ones and especially the hard ones. Looking back, I can see how God's hands were always all over everything that has happened, especially the lessons He taught me through the difficult seasons of my son being diagnosed with autism and losing loved ones. Now I have a renewed hope for the future, knowing He'll be right there beside me, giving grace where I need it most.

—Kim Stewart

I'm not good at looking at myself or my life. *Grace Maps* opened up memories, both good and not so good, of my past that helped me to really see how many times God was walking with me through some of the toughest times. *Grace Maps* also helped me smile at so many sweet memories of where God's handiwork in my life became more obvious. If you struggle with wondering "where is God," *Grace Maps* is a beautiful faith builder to see that He is, and always was, there even when we don't feel Him. Thank you, Carmen, for the road trip.

—Karen Spruell

Grace Maps helped answer and clarify for me personally the old question I've too often pondered, 'Why did bad things happen to an innocent child, in particular, me? Why didn't God intervene, rescue me, punish the perpetrator?'

Developing my Grace Map has been a good, healthy emotional medicine for me. My childhood years, especially, often brought sad memories and frustration. However, the questions posed, guidance given about how to think about my past, and the correlating scriptures provided helped me get a different, healthier perspective on many of these sad memories. Thank you, Carmen, for gifting us with *Grace Maps!!*

—Sherry Martin, Results Coach & Entrepreneur Enthusiast

It's taken me many years to embrace my life story as GOD'S story for my life. Sure, I'd focus on all the good things God led me through, but I'd wonder about the painful hurts, disappointments, failures, and inadequacies. I'm so grateful for Jesus' many questions in the Bible, such as: "What do you want?" Why are you afraid? Which of you, by worrying, can add a single day to your life?" Questions help us think through things and gain perspective. That's exactly what *Grace*

Maps does! The questions help us wrestle with the happenings in our lives so we can see God illuminate how He has been near the whole time and how His hand has guided us through. The result is a real treasure map for our life journey! Stick with it. Think and pray. Let your heart and mind revisit past experiences and listen as God reveals His great love and encouragement!

—Betsy Ringer, Speaker, Author, Mentor

It's truly amazing to be able to navigate our life journey in such an amazing way with *Grace Maps*. It's truly the Grace of God that carries us through our journey, and if we yield the right-of-way to this map and stay on course with the Holy Spirit (GPS), we shall surely arrive at the place called "there" — a land flowing with milk & honey, *Grace Maps* will definitely re-route many to a brighter future in the Kingdom.

—Lucinda Marie Davis

Grace Maps is such a beautiful, special way to learn the Word and take a journey through the Scriptures. I love the map concept as Holy Spirit guides us through His Word through grace. Love it!

—Shelley Odom

When reading Carmen Horne's *Grace Maps,* I was constantly surprised by one important fact in all the life stages: God's Presence. Creating a "life map" in retrospect allowed for the remembrance of past situations coupled with new discoveries of God's continual presence. The "life map" became a Grace Map. What a gift!

—Tammy Lawless

I have thoroughly enjoyed walking through *Grace Maps.* Over the years, I have run across several "life map" processes. While they have been good, *Grace Maps* has excelled! Carmen's approach helped me explore my life from God's perspective, not with my limited vision. I saw that He chose a family for me and placed me in it. Walking through *Grace Maps* opened my eyes to see how the Lord was drawing me, even as a small child, even when I had no knowledge He was there. Thank you, Carmen and *Grace Maps!!*

—Ellen Chauvin

I dedicate this guidebook to my momma. You never missed an opportunity to travel. You could pack your little bag in minutes. So there should have been no surprises for us when Jesus called you to come to live with Him, and you went as fast as you could. Going places was in your DNA. P.S. I sure do miss you.

And to all the women who feel as if they journey their path alone. After creating your personal Grace Map, may your spiritual eyes be opened to God's footprints alongside you through the years.

You are known and loved.

Christie,
I thought of you when I read this.
Carmen is my niece and I love
and respect her Faith very much.
She has been looking for Peace and
Love in her life along with
some answers as to why!
May God Bless you with Love
and Peace! Hugs
Cheryle Wiggins
"Mimi"

Table of Contents

From Me to You....................11

Beginnings....................13

Grace....................16

Beauty from Pain....................18

Memories....................22

Dear Me....................26

Let's Create....................28

Early Childhood – Birth to Twelve....................35

God Uses People....................48

Eternal Perspective....................51

Teen to Young Adult – Thirteen to Twenty....................61

Adult – Twenty-One to Forty....................79

Middle Age – Forty-One to Sixty-Four....................97

The Golden Years – Sixty-Five and Forward....................117

Life Beyond....................125

A Beautifully Crafted Story....................131

Simple Salvation Prayer....................133

Meet the Author....................143

Acknowledgments....................145

Counseling Resources....................147

Carmen's Other Books....................149

Map Key

Use these icons as a simple guide or create your own.

From Me to You

"Let the redeemed of the LORD tell their story..." Psalm 107:2 (NIV)

Have you ever looked intentionally at your life with a panoramic view? As most of us do, I have zoomed in on individual circumstances and events, especially tough situations, with regularity. However, viewing my journey with an eternal perspective — a big picture lens — has not happened consistently.

Over the years, I have thought about my life timeline. Recently, my occasional thought became an exciting challenge. How can I create a process to help us see God's divine care for us, even through the pea-soup fog of difficulties? We need a tangible reminder. We need *Grace Maps.*

What if the unexpected delays and detours in our lives are not random? *Grace Maps* takes us on a journey to uncover God's grace in every situation of our lives. Too often, we believe the things we face happen to us and assume God is silent. In reality, our lives are a well-planned journey, and the detours and roadblocks are divine directions and recalculations because of personal choices. *Grace Maps* is our guidebook to help us better understand how connecting our past journey with our present course reveals God's consistent presence along our life path.

Reading maps has never been my thing. Tasking me with the navigation on a trip will probably mean ten seconds after we pass the exit I will say, "Oh wait! I think that was our exit." I'm a planner that can get off the plan when an opportunity for a good spell of visitin' presents itself. Thank goodness we now carry GPS wherever we go on our mobile phones. My lady is named Lola. She has no problem saying, "Turn around," or, "Make a U-turn when possible." Lola is the keeper of the map.

So, you can see how creating a map of my life was a challenge. I can become sidetracked and get caught up in areas that need a map the size of a world atlas to adequately diagram the situation. But I did contain myself, and now I have a written testimony of God's goodness through the years. That's what I want for you – a written testimony.

God has been so good to you. Are you in a spot where you can realize that?

In Matthew 28:16-20, Jesus commissioned each believer to present the Good News, Jesus' offer of salvation, to all.

Along with that, for me, comes equipping the saints, specifically women. God has offered me many pathways to encourage His girls. Yet, my ministry has gradually begun to focus on the power of our perspective. A change of perspective is not something I simply study but a practice I'm learning to live.

Our stories are powerful when we share our personal experiences with the proper perspective. When you think about planning a vacation, you want to hear reviews from people you know who have actually been where you're going. It is no different with our life journeys. Sharing our stories of God's grace for our journey will help those navigating similar circumstances. Your story brings hope to the next generation of road-weary travelers.

As we begin, may I pray for you, for us?

Heavenly Father,

Your Word tells us in Revelation 12:11 that we overcome Satan's influence in our lives by our relationship with Your Son, Jesus, and our testimony. Help us see our lives with an eternal perspective. Comfort us when we are sad and fill us with joy as we see Your hand guiding us throughout our lives. Let not one moment of pain be of no gain. Use each of our stories as the backdrop that illustrates Your providential care. Hold our hand, sweet Lord. We depend on You!

We ask all these things in the mighty Name of Jesus Christ. Amen!

Your personal Grace Map is a creative way to see life as a beautiful memoir instead of a series of short stories. So why don't we create one together?

With great anticipation,

Carmen

2022

Beginnings

I praise you, for I am fearfully and wonderfully made. Wonderful are your works; my soul knows it very well. Psalm 139:14 (ESV)

The day I was born seemed like a good day for a party. My parents were barely adults. At that age, when your friends want to pile up (southern for gather) in your room, eat hamburgers, and laugh loudly, there seems to be no reason to stop the fun — unless you were born in the 1960s. Did you know there was a "no fun in childbirth" rule during that era?

I doubt any of us can remember the day of our birth, but most of us have probably heard stories about that day. Maybe you are adopted and don't have details about your day of delivery. Please take a moment to recall what you have been told about your adoptive parents' excitement as they met you and you became their child. No matter the details, not one of us is an accident.

> "You saw me before I was born. Every day of my life was recorded in your book. Every moment was laid out before a single day had passed." Psalm 139:16 (NLT)

In Rick Warren's book, *The Purpose Driven Life,* he offers an explanation that may put those of us who were unplanned at ease, "While there are illegitimate parents, there are no illegitimate children. Many children are unplanned by their parents, but they are not unplanned by God. God's purpose took into account human error and even sin."[1] Thank you, Pastor Warren.

Since our Creator intricately plans all our births, let's pause to celebrate. Today may be the very first time you realize this freeing fact. Let me repeat it. You are not a mess-up or a mistake. You are born for your generation, at your place of birth, and into your family. God may not have trusted your biological parents to raise you, but He used their DNA to create you. If this brought tears to your eyes, that's OK.

Your salty tears will help heal the wounds that often come with wondering if anyone wanted you to squeal your first cry.

How does the understanding that you are not an accident or mistake make you feel?

Read Zephaniah 3:17 and write it here.

1 Dr. Rick Warren, *The Purpose Driven Life,* Zondervan, 2002, 23

God was one happy Daddy when you were born. He did not pass out cigars, but He wrote you a beautiful lullaby that He continues to sing over you daily.

Speak the scriptural affirmation I provide in each section over yourself when you need a little reminder of how your Daddy God feels about you.

Scriptural Affirmation:

I am not a mistake. God planned every moment of my life before my birth. I bring Him delight, and He sings a beautiful song over me. (cf *Psalm 139:16, Zephaniah 3:17)*

Our mommas listened intently as their doctors confirmed what most of them already suspected; a new life had begun within them. And just like our mommas, a young peasant girl named Mary was also given a life-changing proclamation when the angel Gabriel visited her to announce she was pregnant. Jesus' birth was a surprise to Mary but not to Father God. Jesus' human, earthly beginning ushered in the greatest gift of grace we will ever experience.

> "This means that anyone who belongs to Christ has become a new person. The old life is gone; a new life has begun!" 2 Corinthians 5:17 (NLT)

After Gabriel's announcement, Mary responded with faith, trust, and the belief that God's grace would help her meet every challenge — the challenges she knew she would confront and the struggles she could not yet comprehend. Challenges await us all, even along the paths God gives us the green light to travel.

> "And Mary said, 'Behold, I am the servant of the Lord; let it be to me according to your word.'" Luke 1:38 (ESV)

Unknowns are certain in beginnings. Unknown to us but not unknown to God. Looking back over Mary's life, we see God's gift of grace carried her through the ups and downs of her journey. As we reflect on our lives, we will also see God's sustaining hands of grace carrying us. (2 Corinthians 12:9).

GRACE

"So let us come boldly to the throne of our gracious God. There we will receive his mercy, and we will find grace to help us when we need it the most." Hebrews 4:16 (NLT)

Why would I name the journey we will travel in our guidebook *Grace Maps?* The writer of Hebrews offers a glimpse of my thoughts when he speaks of God's grace helping us when we need it most. In need of help pretty much describes our lives, right?

God's grace is not only His offer of salvation to all. It is His ongoing willingness to walk with us every day. His grace equips us, strengthens us, and empowers us to live a life that brings Him glory and offers us the benefits of abundant life.

I have heard it said that mercy is not getting what we deserve, and grace is getting what we don't deserve. Grace is God's unconditional love for us — even though we don't deserve it. The gift of unmerited favor.

God paves His divine path for our lives with grace. He knows we are human (Psalm 103:14) and understands our need for His saving grace, not only at our initial profession of faith in Him but every step of every day. Ephesians 2:10 says, "For we are God's masterpiece. He has created us anew in Christ Jesus, so we can do the good things he planned for us long ago." (NLT)

We are created new in Christ by God's grace, and by His grace, we can walk along His path for our lives.

Your Grace Map is a tangible reminder of your Heavenly Father's presence from before your first breath to where you stand today.

Ephesians 2:8 says, "For by grace you have been saved through faith. And this is not your own doing; it is the gift of God." (ESV)

Have you accepted Jesus Christ as your Savior? If you have not, He awaits you. Our relationship with Jesus is our foundation. He is also our Healer. He empowers us to renew our minds.

If you want to know more about receiving Jesus Christ as your Savior, your guidebook has a simple salvation prayer in the back.

If you prayed a prayer asking Jesus to be your Savior, you are now a member of the family of God. Welcome to the family! Let's celebrate if you have been a Christ-follower for one minute or one hundred years. **In the space below, write a prayer of thanksgiving to God for your salvation and His love for you.**

BEAUTY FROM PAIN

God helps us recognize the beauty in our pain. Here are a few questions you might ask yourself as you meander along the path of your Grace Map and uncover tender places:

- Can I look at this event/situation from a different perspective?
- How can I describe this differently than I have in the past?
- Did anything good happen?
- Did I learn any valuable lessons?
- Can I see how God worked through this difficult time?
- Does it look different now, looking back?
- Have I been able to help someone else with my testimony?

When (I say when because we all have them) you wander into a painful spot, take a moment to search your heart. Then, if you are not ready to look at that tender spot with any depth, give it a name on your map and move on.

Heartbreak comes to us differently. Each of us will make our list. I pray that in every painful time of your life, Jesus will open your eyes to His presence.

Our Grace Maps not only contain our past, but they also include our present. We will chart our lives up to the present time. Fortunately, we don't know the specifics of our future. If we did, our hearts might fail us or become filled with arrogance and pride, as my mom would say, "Too big for our britches." God declares that only He knows our future. He purposely keeps some things secret. Why? The knowing could discourage us to the point of quitting or entice us to move in our timing instead of God's. Instead, we can rest peacefully knowing God's promise in Jeremiah 29:11; He has gone before us, and His plans are good.

We have assurances about the future of a surrendered life. God will finish what He has started in us. I love Philippians 1:6, and I think you will, too. **Write it out below:**

The beginning of our journey is a great time to let you in on a secret. Only a secret because the Church doesn't often discuss it. It's OK to seek professional Christian counseling. There's nothing unspiritual about it, and I have significantly benefited from an excellent Christian counselor's healing words. God uses people as His hands and feet in this old world. Sometimes I wonder why He would trust us with such important tasks, but He does. I have included some resources to help you take the first step toward healing with a Christian counselor at the end of the book.

I am confident the Bible supports seeking the counsel of other godly people. The book of Proverbs has many verses that offer confirmation. Take a moment to read these: Proverbs 11:14; Proverbs 12:15; Proverbs 15:22. Proverbs 19:20 reminds us how advice and wisdom are connected. **So please take a moment and write it out below.**

The Apostle Paul offers a process of comfort in his second letter to the Corinthians:

God comforts us in our pain, and we share His comfort by comforting others in their pain.

> "Blessed be the God and Father of our Lord Jesus Christ, the Father of mercies and God of all comfort, who comforts us in all our affliction, so that we may be able to comfort those who are in any affliction, with the comfort with which we ourselves are comforted by God. For as we share abundantly in Christ's sufferings, so through Christ we share abundantly in comfort too."
> 2 Corinthians 1:3-5 (ESV)

Sometimes you will never know the value of
a moment, until it becomes a memory.

—*Dr. Seuss*

MEMORIES

As I write today, my heart still aches over the death of my sweet and sassy momma. Over the last few years, my memories have comforted me. My sister and I have touched every earthly possession she owned — clothes, shoes, purses, and enough costume jewelry to open a store. And y'all, all the pictures and little mementos. We spent days wandering through the things she loved enough to keep. We laughed and cried.

Friends, memories will do that to you. Sometimes they make you smile, and sometimes you can't speak because tears have robbed you of breath. So I want you to be prepared to feel all the feels as you look back over your life.

There will be times that we may need comfort from The Comforter during this process. We need not walk one step without His help.

In John 14:15-31, Jesus promises His disciples, including you and I, the Holy Spirit. **Read the passage and record what you learn about Him in these Scriptures.**

The Holy Spirit is a gentleman. He awaits your invitation to walk with you. He will guide you and your memories. The Bible assures us that God wants to direct our steps.

> "The heart of man plans his way, but the Lord establishes his steps" Proverbs 16:9 (ESV)

Take a moment and request His presence in prayer. **Then, feel free to write your prayer in the space on the next page.**

Before creating my first Grace Map, I was fretting over my memory. I can't remember much of my childhood— at least not in detail. I was concerned that if I couldn't fill in the blanks, my Grace Map would look more like a map of the Mojave Desert. Then, God brought John 14:26 to my attention. Did you catch that verse when we read it earlier? Let's pause so you can reread it. I'll wait.

Isn't that a wonderful verse? I have heard the Holy Spirit called the Great Reminder. He will help us call to mind what we need to remember. So, relax. You will be surprised how much is stored in the crevices of your mind for you to find.

Let us pray together:

Lord, help us remember any event You can use for our testimony. Guide our memory. Bring us joy in this process. Help us giggle at the good times and be thankful for your presence in the difficult ones. May any tears we shed be tears of joy over Your goodness and grace.

In Jesus' Name. Amen.

Today I know that such memories are the key not to the past, but to the future. I know that the experiences of our lives, when we let God use them, become the mysterious and perfect preparation for the work he will give us to do.

—Corrie Ten Boom

DEAR ME

I like to go back and read my old journal entries. Do you? They are like snapshots of my life at particular times and markers of how far the Lord has brought me. He never lets me down and far exceeds my expectations.

Will you take a moment before you get started and write a letter to yourself describing what you hope, dream, and pray that the Holy Spirit will do within you as you look back to move forward? So often, at the beginning of a study, I write a letter, and by the conclusion, I can say, look what the Lord has done in me!

Dear Me,

When I have finished my Grace Map, I

LET'S CREATE

It's time to be creative. No worries if you are like me and can't draw a straight line. Thank You, Lord, for rulers! You can illustrate your Grace Map in as much detail as you choose. I'll give you some tips along the way. Be bold. Use magazine clippings, stickers, and maybe even whip out your colored pencils and draw.

At the end of each life stage, I have included pages to create your Grace Map for that stage. There is a link at the end of the book to get a printable Grace Map template. You can take your smaller maps and combine them into one beautiful drawing.

On your piece of paper, draw a horizontal line (like the one on page 30), leaving a margin on each end and room on the top and bottom of your line. You need space to write.

Remember, your line will be much larger than my example. It needs to be proportional to your map size. Keep this in mind as you decide on your paper size when combining all your smaller Grace Maps into a larger one. You can use butcher paper, blank paper taped together, or art paper from your local craft store to create your map. Go for what you love! I am setting you free on design. If you are interested in a beautifully designed map template to create your personal Grace Map, you will find a free one on Carmen's book page, www.gracemapsbook.com.

We will divide our map into five stages of life:

- Early Childhood (birth to twelve)
- Teen/Young Adult (thirteen to twenty)
- Adult (twenty-one to forty)
- Middle Age (forty-one to sixty-four)
- The Golden Years (sixty-five and forward)

Feel free to work through these stages back-to-back if you can set aside a whole day to create or in smaller chunks of time spread out over several weeks. If you haven't reached one of the stages, you can stop your Grace Map with your current season. Or, you can spend some time contemplating how you would like to answer the questions in your future seasons when you do arrive. Be sure to read "Life Beyond" and "A Beautifully Crafted Story" to finish well.

As you answer the questions about each stage of life, you will gather information to add to your Grace Map. You may want to use your journal for overflow answers or the pages I have provided in the back of the book for notes.

I think we can all agree that our vantage point here on earth can be pretty limited compared to God's view of the world. The ultimate goal for our *Grace Maps* is to see our lives with a panoramic view. We want to lay down stones of remembrance to enable us to recognize God's faithfulness and grace toward us in every leg of the journey. You can read more about how God commanded the Israelites to erect stones of remembrance after crossing the Jordan River into the promised land in Joshua 4:19.

Remember, you don't have to answer every question. I provide them to prompt your memory. If you think of important milestones not covered in the questions, feel free to make notes of them, too.

You can see an example of a Grace Map on the following pages.

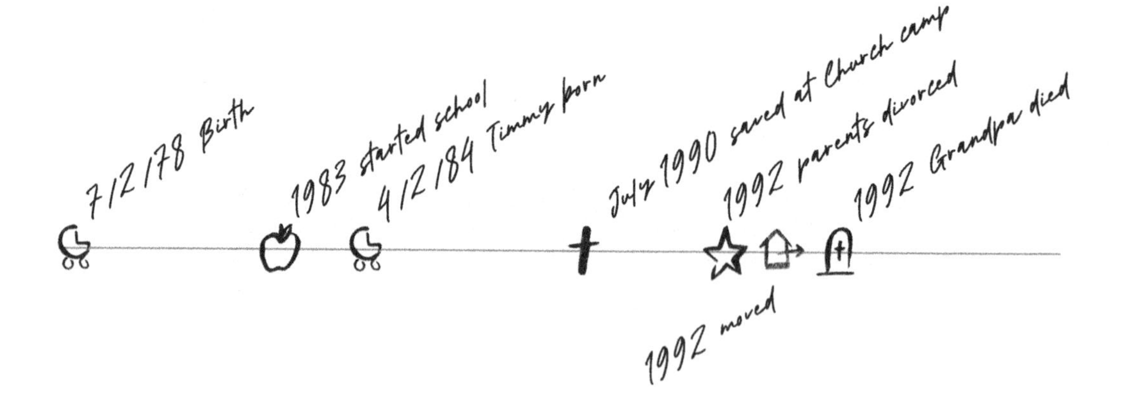

Use this space to summarize how you now see God working in your life during these years.

I see God working in my life as a child when he placed love of church camp in my heart. I began attending when I was old enough to go and got saved at church camp just two years before my parents were divorced. He knew I would need the support of my church and the Holy Spirit in my heart to not fall into the wrong crowd and mess my life up.

1994 C.J. broke my heart

1996 graduated HS

1996 1st job

12/24/98 got married

"A person's a person, no matter how small."

—Dr. Seuss

Early Childhood – Birth to Twelve

"For you formed my inward parts; you knitted me together in my mother's womb." Psalm 139:13 (ESV)

I gained a new appreciation for pregnancy and midwifery by watching some episodes of the PBS show *Call the Midwife*. These women are on the front line. They must think fast and be creative problem-solvers while treating mommy and daddy compassionately. Y'all, that's a tough job.

Personally, one of the reasons I know I was born at the perfect time is the tremendous medical strides in obstetrics over the years. By the time I delivered our sweet girl, a woman had options. Epidural anesthesia during childbirth can make you want to kiss the doctor. Back in the day, like the days of Abraham and Sarah, you sat on a birthing stool (rock or stone situated under each hiney cheek) and pushed. The midwife literally caught your young'un. Is that TMI?

My ears perk up when the Old Testament mentions women by name. For example, in the book of Exodus, we meet two midwives God used to stop Hebrew infanticide in epic proportions.

Pharaoh's command to Shiphrah and Puah was clear — "If the child is a son, kill him." He felt his evil plan for population control would secure his power. But the midwives were smart women. Though Pharaoh had the power to kill them, they disobeyed his edict. Why? They feared God more than they feared Pharoah. The midwives had seen God work miraculously throughout their lives and careers. They knew God was in ultimate control. You can read about these two heroes in Exodus 1:15-21.

Shiphrah and Puah offered hope to the parents of the babies they helped deliver. Those Hebrew boys would have a birth story to tell that would be hard to top. Now, let's take some time and discover your birth story.

Record your full name at the top of your map.

Have you researched the meaning of your name? If so, what is it?

Were you told stories about how your parents chose your name?

Do you have a nickname? How did it originate?

Did any surprising or sensational events happen at or around your birth?

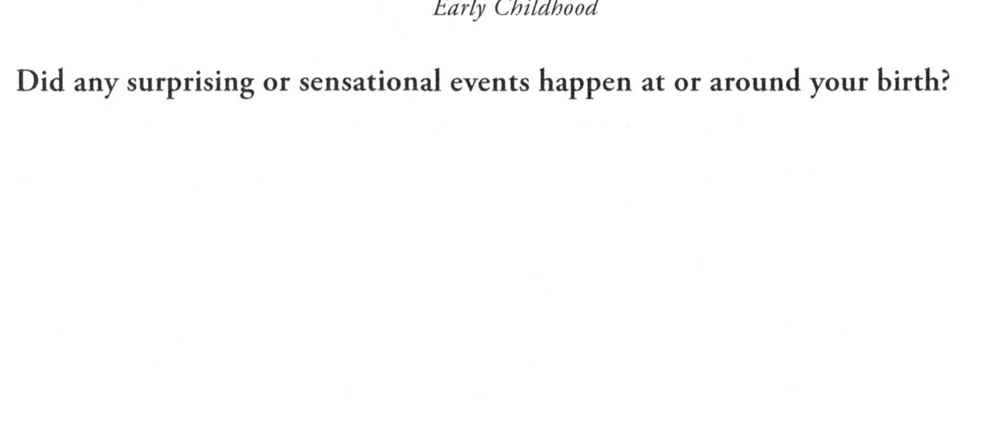

I was a wee bit premature, weighing a whopping five+ pounds. My momma told me she carried me on a pillow, fearing she would drop me. I had a tummy ache from birth. I'm sure I tried my young mommy's nerves.

Mom was not married to my dad when she became pregnant. That very fact placed her in a difficult situation in 1959. Women still face difficult decisions with unplanned pregnancies.

Before I was born, they married, and we began our lives together as a family of three. I'm so very thankful Mom decided I was a risk she was willing to take.

In Psalm 139:11-16, David, by Holy Spirit inspiration, beautifully expresses God's complete knowledge of us. **Take a moment to recount our Creator God's intimate planning for our lives long before birth.**

I'm the firstborn. Where do you fall in birth order?

Did any critical or central events happen in your life from birth to twelve years? (i.e., divorce, deaths, births, salvation, moving, changing schools, friends lost or gained, etc.)

Consider world events, too. When Mordecai encouraged Esther to use her position to help the Hebrew people, he reminded her it was very possible she was queen for this very reason — "for such a time as this" (Esther 4:14). Our births are not coincidental but purposeful. We are created for a specific time and place.

Be sensitive as you record personal events and interactions. You may want to identify people without using their names. Use something you will recognize but others will not. God's grace helps us understand what information will be more harmful than helpful.

As a young child, did you understand what was happening during the events you recorded above?

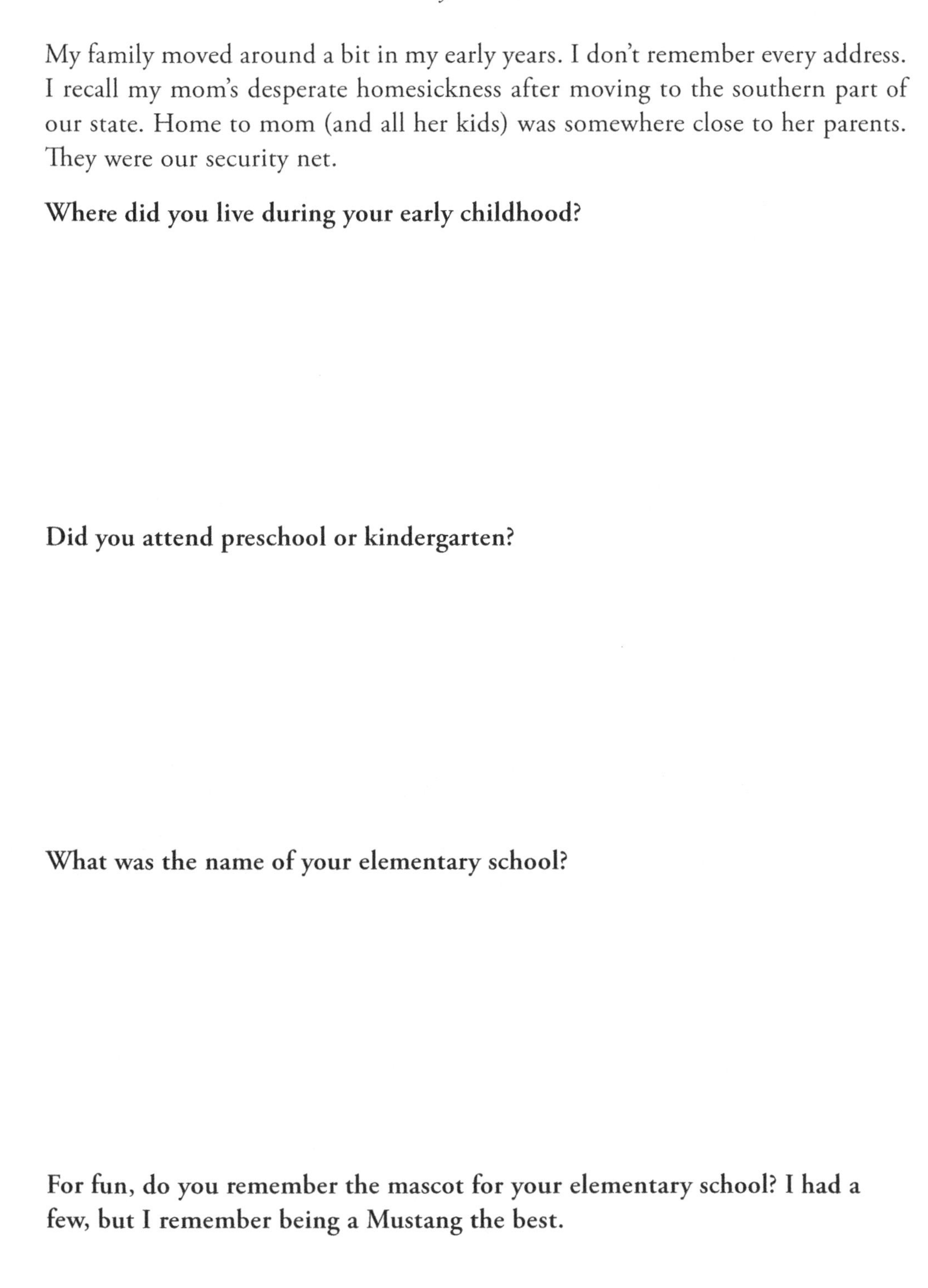

My family moved around a bit in my early years. I don't remember every address. I recall my mom's desperate homesickness after moving to the southern part of our state. Home to mom (and all her kids) was somewhere close to her parents. They were our security net.

Where did you live during your early childhood?

Did you attend preschool or kindergarten?

What was the name of your elementary school?

For fun, do you remember the mascot for your elementary school? I had a few, but I remember being a Mustang the best.

Did you consider yourself a good student?

What was your favorite subject? Least favorite?

What were your hobbies during your early childhood?

Did you have a favorite toy or game? What made them so special to you?

Who was your best friend?

Can you recount a fun memory you made with your best friend?

I attended an Elvis Presley concert. Momma bought me a cute outfit to wear. I mean, I had to look cute — just in case Elvis saw me among those thousand other fans!

Did your family travel or take vacations?

What is your happiest memory during this time?

What is your most difficult memory?

At age nine, I experienced one of my most difficult memories. My dad was sitting on the couch as mom moved us out of our family home. I cannot forget his words, "I won't get to see y'all very often." Reliving that moment brings a lump to my throat. My mom and dad's divorce made a significant impact on my life. They divorced, and after a while, we didn't see him as often as we did when they first separated. Their relationship was so dysfunctional. I don't know how they could have stayed married. I was way too young to figure that out, yet I wanted them together, just like many children of divorce.

Reflecting on your own personal experiences and what others told you about your family dynamics, what effects might the emotional atmosphere of your family in early childhood have on you?

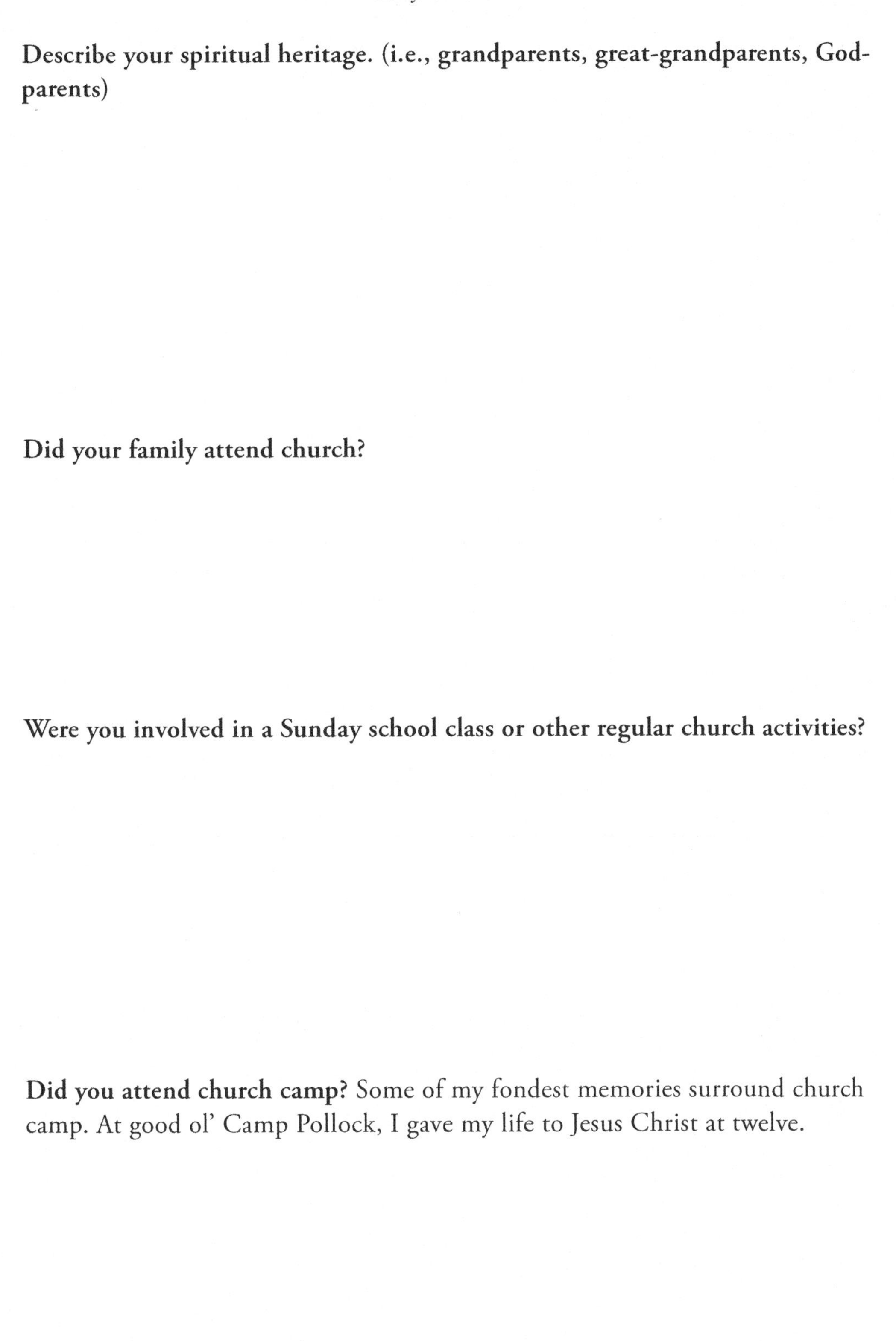

Describe your spiritual heritage. (i.e., grandparents, great-grandparents, God-parents)

Did your family attend church?

Were you involved in a Sunday school class or other regular church activities?

Did you attend church camp? Some of my fondest memories surround church camp. At good ol' Camp Pollock, I gave my life to Jesus Christ at twelve.

What is the most powerful lesson God taught you during this time?

How would you describe your relationship with God during the first twelve years of your life?

Who made the most significant positive impact on you during your early childhood?

Can you recall a truth given by this person that you still have tucked away in your heart today?

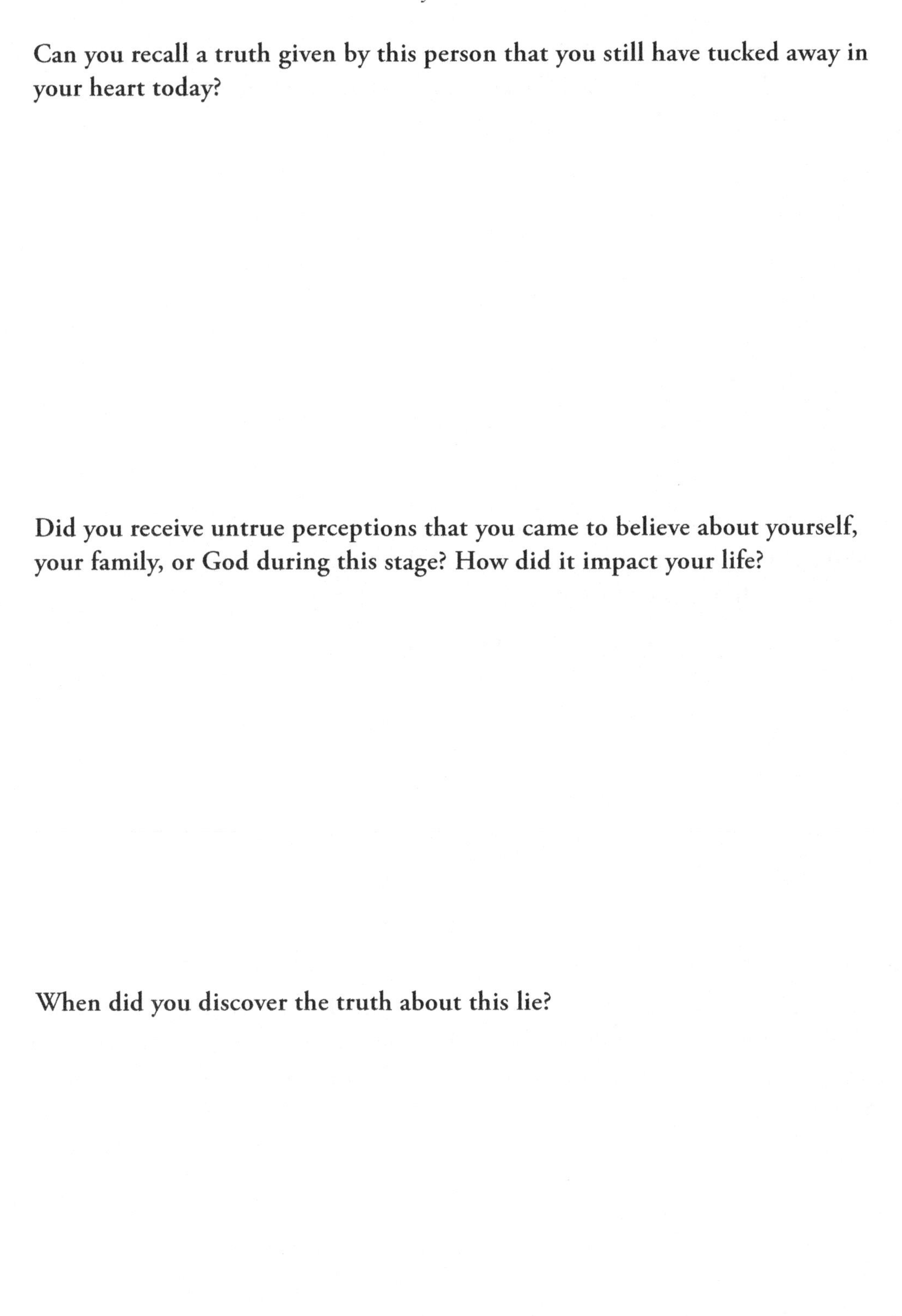

Did you receive untrue perceptions that you came to believe about yourself, your family, or God during this stage? How did it impact your life?

When did you discover the truth about this lie?

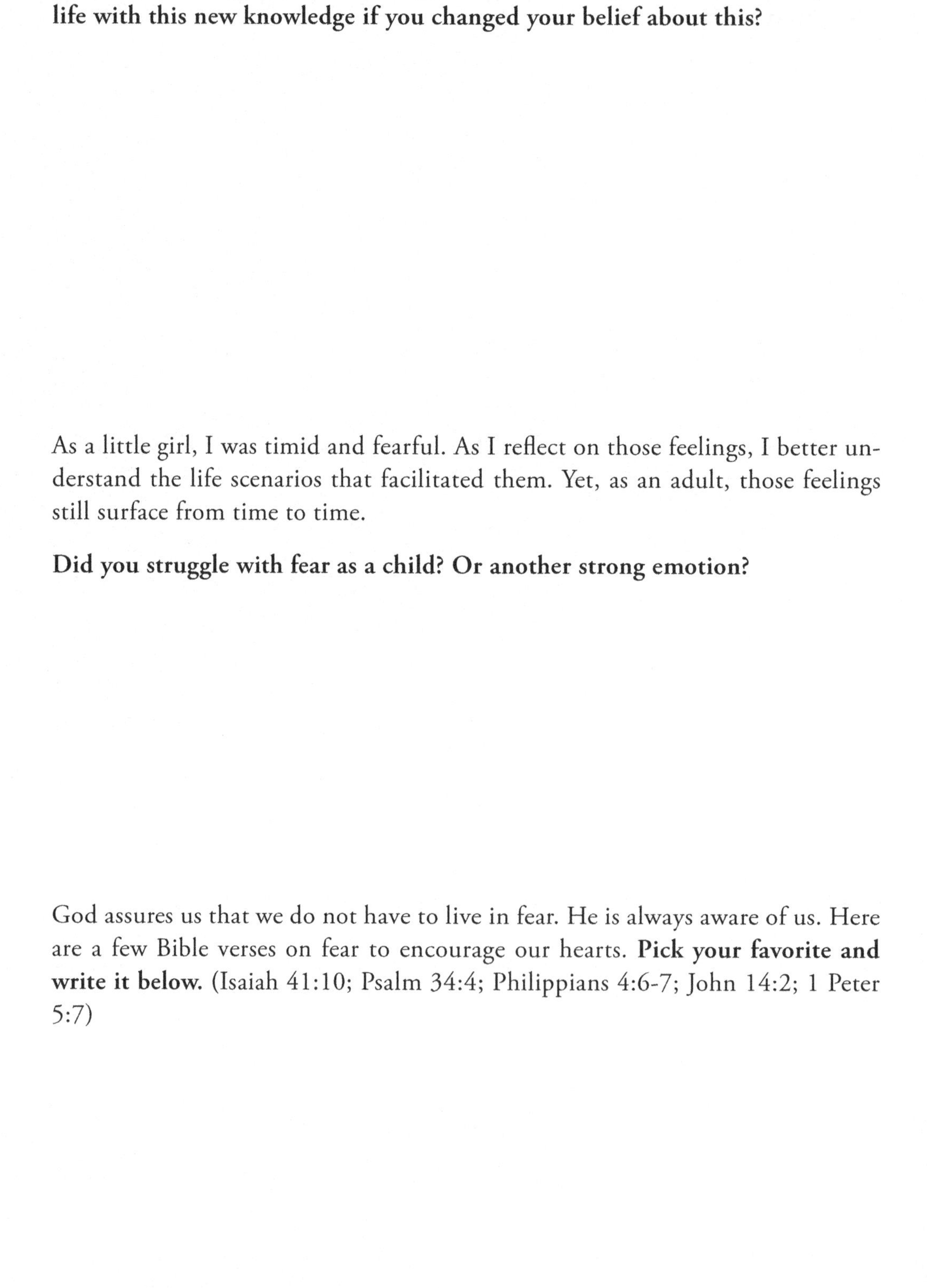

Do you still struggle with believing this lie? How might God transform your life with this new knowledge if you changed your belief about this?

As a little girl, I was timid and fearful. As I reflect on those feelings, I better understand the life scenarios that facilitated them. Yet, as an adult, those feelings still surface from time to time.

Did you struggle with fear as a child? Or another strong emotion?

God assures us that we do not have to live in fear. He is always aware of us. Here are a few Bible verses on fear to encourage our hearts. **Pick your favorite and write it below.** (Isaiah 41:10; Psalm 34:4; Philippians 4:6-7; John 14:2; 1 Peter 5:7)

How do these promises make you feel?

GOD USES PEOPLE

It was in my early childhood that a friend's dad molested me. Can I tell you that looking for the good in that time of my life has taken lots of pondering? Over the years, though, I have come to recognize God's protection.

My early life was a bit topsy-turvy. I had a stable mom, but my dad wasn't ready to be a dad or husband. So a secure place for me was my maternal grandparent's home. I visited as often as Mom would allow. She frequently asked, "Why do you like to stay there so much? What do you do there that is so much fun?" My only answer at that time was, "I just like it."

My papaw would lay his rough hand on my forehead every overnight visit and pray the sweetest prayer. Y'all, that was so comforting to this scaredy-cat little girl. I felt so insecure and insignificant, but his presence helped me sleep peacefully. My papaw moved in with Jesus in 1991, and God continues to answer his prayers for me.

I didn't understand the significance of papaw's prayers then. But, in retrospect, I see God at work through him.

When I reflect on the first twelve years of my life, I recognize the beginnings of my relationship with God. A one-sided relationship began with God loving and seeking me, and as I grew older, our relationship became a mutual desire for connection. God's love for us stirs our hearts to return His love (1 John 4:19).

Can you see how God worked on your behalf during your early childhood?

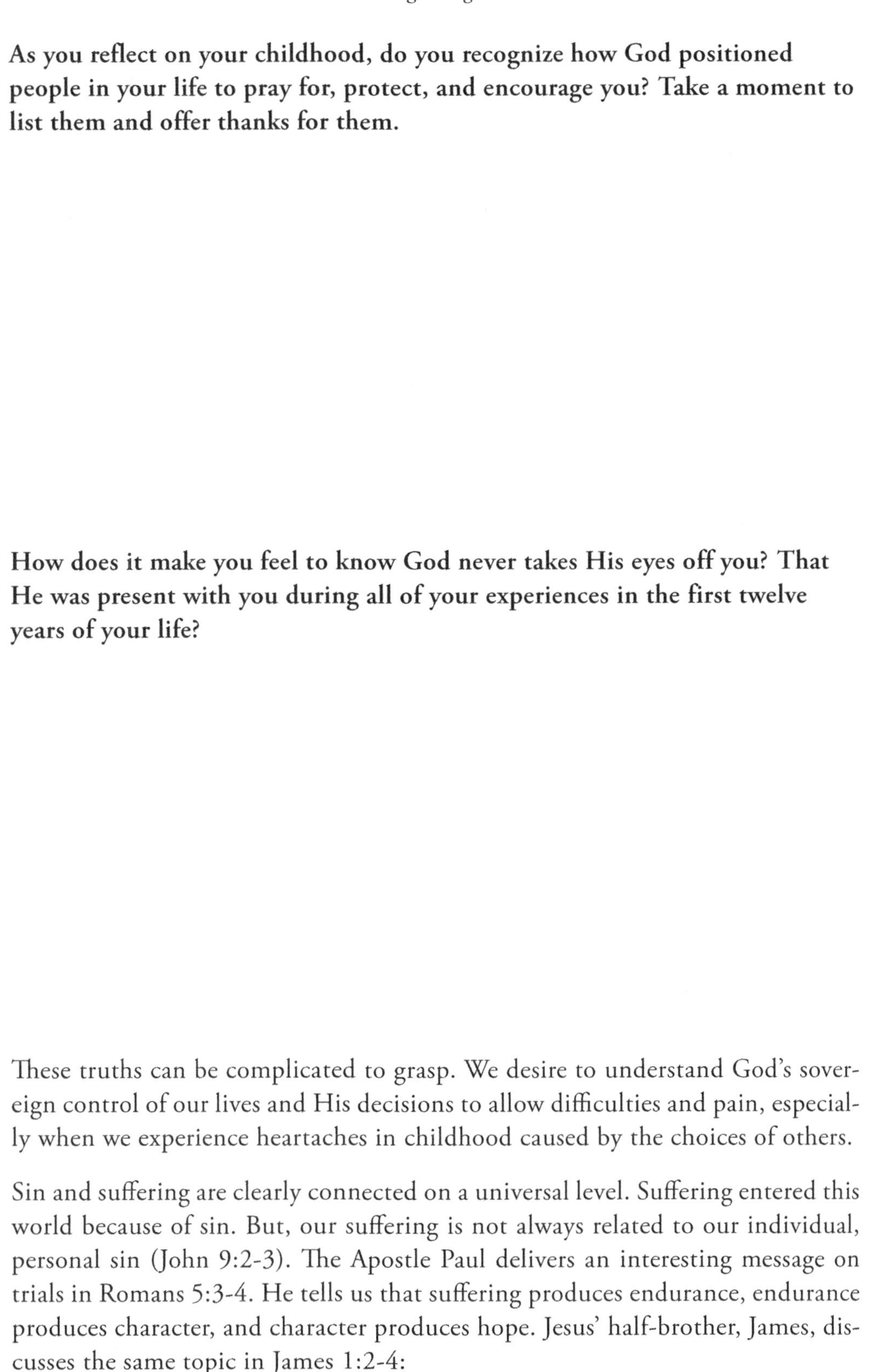

As you reflect on your childhood, do you recognize how God positioned people in your life to pray for, protect, and encourage you? Take a moment to list them and offer thanks for them.

How does it make you feel to know God never takes His eyes off you? That He was present with you during all of your experiences in the first twelve years of your life?

These truths can be complicated to grasp. We desire to understand God's sovereign control of our lives and His decisions to allow difficulties and pain, especially when we experience heartaches in childhood caused by the choices of others.

Sin and suffering are clearly connected on a universal level. Suffering entered this world because of sin. But, our suffering is not always related to our individual, personal sin (John 9:2-3). The Apostle Paul delivers an interesting message on trials in Romans 5:3-4. He tells us that suffering produces endurance, endurance produces character, and character produces hope. Jesus' half-brother, James, discusses the same topic in James 1:2-4:

> "Count it all joy, my brothers, when you meet trials of various kinds, for you know that the testing of your faith produces steadfastness. And let steadfastness have its full effect, that you may be perfect and complete, lacking in nothing." (ESV)

I can't explain how the redemption of pain works for us as Christians. Our Bible has many personal redemption stories. I have witnessed and heard testimonies of God transforming bad situations into good outcomes. God has redeemed pain and suffering in my life, and my faith in God's goodness gives me comfort that He will continue to redeem my pain until He carries me to my eternal home. John reminds us in the book of Revelation that there is a better day ahead—this is what I call an eternal perspective.

> "He will wipe every tear from their eyes, and there will be no more death or sorrow or crying or pain. All these things are gone forever." Revelation 21:4 (NLT)

ETERNAL PERSPECTIVE

Romans 8:28 is another foundational verse for looking at our lives through an eternal perspective lens.

> "And we know that God causes everything to work together for the good of those who love God and are called according to his purposes for them" Romans 8:28 (NLT)

Romans 8:28 is a reminder that God does have a good plan for our lives, and He will use many different means, even those events that feel painful as we trudge through them, to see it come to pass. I'm certainly not a theologian, but let's break down this verse just a bit.

Causes and work together — synergeō (this word is similar to our word synergy) is the transliteration of causes and work together. Blue Letter Bible Online[2] states that Strong's Concordance defines this as fellow-worker, cooperate, help with, and assist.

Purposes — prothesis. This word indeed means a purpose — setting forth of a thing — placing it in view.

Occasionally, I like to paraphrase verses using the expanded definitions of the Greek words to guide my understanding, but never to replace actual Scripture. For example, my paraphrase of this verse reads like this: "and we know that God as our fellow-worker, assists everything (all — good and bad) to work together for the good of those who love Him and are called (Invited. God invites us all to His Kingdom.) according to the specific purpose God set forth in advance for them."

How would you rewrite Romans 8:28 in your own words?

2 https://www.blueletterbible.org/lexicon/g4903/kjv (June 1, 2021)

Paul's letter to the Ephesians (1:11) echoes Romans 8:28. He writes, "Furthermore, because we are united with Christ, we have received an inheritance from God, for he chose us in advance, and he makes everything work out according to his plan." (NLT)

We cannot understand the providence of God. We will never wrap our minds around His purposes for us or how He makes decisions about what He allows in His children's lives. Sometimes, I wish I could understand. But then I came to my senses and realized that my heart would surely faint if I knew my future. Wouldn't yours?

I'm going to confirm what you already know; finding something useful in a stormy, life-wrecking situation can take time — a fair amount of time. And, even then, it may only be the tiniest sliver of hope.

Stormy times are when faith matters most. These times are when the beginning of Romans 8:28, "And we know," comforts us the most. Because when we know, we can begin to see our stormy situations through an eternal lens. We can trust God to work out all the details and approach the wind and waves with hope and peace.

The Holy Spirit teaches us; one of the main tools He uses is our Bible. He is the Great Revealer. The truths of Psalm 34:15 and 1 Peter 3:12 are powerful affirmations over our lives. They reinforce to us that we have God's attention and focus. **Pause to read them and record their truth below.**

Looking back with a perspective of God's constant presence and attentiveness, do you see painful times differently now?

Did you learn any valuable lessons?

Have you been able to use your childhood testimony to help someone else?

The stage of life, birth to twelve years, is filled with growth. We begin our physical, mental, emotional, and spiritual development that will continue for a lifetime. Habits are forming, and we embark on the journey of becoming distinct personalities with all the intricacies of a unique creation of God. These are the years that are the most carefree for many of us. Some memories from this stage are painful, though; much of that pain could be from being let down by those we should have been able to trust when we were in our most vulnerable years. Our Abba Father is always angry when someone harms His children (Matthew 18:6). Remember, looking back may be painful but looking back also allows us to see God's ever-present help and enduring love.

Let's pause so you can add some details to your map. Answering the questions above about your early childhood memories will offer points of interest for your Grace Map.

Remember, you don't have to answer every question. I provide each one to prompt your memory.

Scriptural Affirmation:

Jesus invites me to come to Him without hindrance. He blesses me because I am His child. (cf *Mark 10:13-16)*

"The things that make me different are
the things that make me, me."

– *Piglet*

Use this space to summarize how you now see God working in your life during these years.

Early Childhood

Optional Map Key

 House  Birth  Grad  Salvation AΩ God  Job

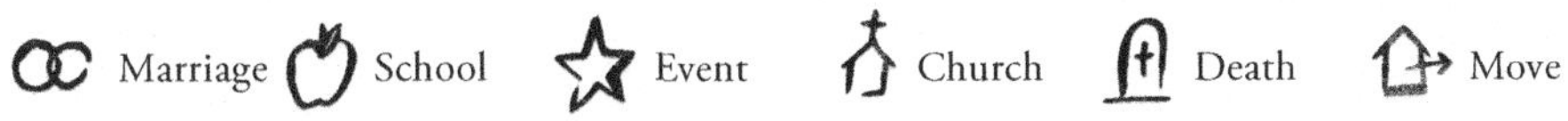

Marriage School Event Church Death Move

"Discovering the truth about ourselves is a lifetime's work, but it's worth the effort."

— Fred Rogers

Teen to Young Adult – Thirteen to Twenty

"So, no matter what I say, what I believe, and what I do, I'm bankrupt without love." 1 Corinthians 13:3 (MSG)

The young maid was stolen, taken from her home as a spoil of war. Kidnapped and dragged away by the Syrians, she found herself at the slave market in Damascus. Everything she held dear, everyone she loved, jerked away. In a physical sense, her Hebrew home was a memory. She was among strangers. Can you imagine how filled with fear she must have been? No doubt, tears washed her eyes every night.

Many of the stolen girls worked the fields, but the great commander, Naaman, purchased our girl as a maid for his wife. God had given him great victory on the battlefield, but his body was losing the war with leprosy.

Our young maid may have been far from home, but she was never far from God's care. She would have learned as a child the stories of how God had freed her people, and we can only imagine that knowledge held her little heart together during the most challenging times.

She gained favor with her captors. As our maiden cared for her mistress each day, she listened to her mistress's brokenhearted lament over her husband's dread disease. The prognosis of a man with leprosy in those days was not only life-altering but fatal.

Although held against her will, our maiden cared about the health of her masters. A beautiful picture of Matthew 5:43-47 (MSG):

> "You're familiar with the old written law, 'Love your friend,' and its unwritten companion, 'Hate your enemy.' I'm challenging that. I'm telling you to love your enemies. Let them bring out the best in you, not the worst. When someone gives you a hard time, respond with the energies of prayer, for then you are working out of your true selves, your God-created selves. This is what God does. He gives his best—the sun to warm and the rain to nourish—to everyone, regardless: the good and bad, the nice and nasty. If all you do is love the lovable, do you expect a bonus? Anybody can do that. If you simply say hello to those who greet you, do you expect a medal? Any run-of-the-mill sinner does that.'"

This young teen girl was in a situation that she did not choose. I'm positive she felt powerless. When she pondered her abduction, she surely wondered how this awful circumstance would unfold. The benefits of being placed in Naaman's home were undoubtedly unclear to her, especially initially. Yet, in her placement, we see God's providential care. Her willingness to help her master find healing opened his eyes to the truth that "there is no God in all the world except in Israel." (2 Kings 5:15 NLT)

Can you imagine being in such a predicament — giving lifesaving information to your kidnappers? Your captors? Thankfully, most of us will never face her situation. We can't know how we would handle such adversity. (Read her story in 2 Kings 5)

Our maiden was probably an early teen, and we all remember those days.

Can we talk about our teen years?

First kisses, first dates, first love, and the first realization that pimples will probably appear on game night or picture day — even with the constant use of acne medication — help describe the teen/young adult years. My teen years were like your teen years. Complicated.

Three memories always come to mind when I consider my junior high years.

I lost my bathing suit bottoms while diving into a pool filled with the school newspaper staff. Maybe that's why I have made it my life's mission to expand my hipline so that bathing suits now must be peeled off of them.

I flung one of my knee-high white boots into the crowd while doing a routine with the drill team. That's probably why my calves are now too big to wear boots.

And my ears were pierced (without my mom's permission) at my friend's mom's beauty shop with a sewing needle and an ink dot to mark the spot. Other teens (boys and girls) surrounded me so I couldn't faint or scream. Instead, I sat in silent agony.

Record a funny memory from your teen years.

Other memories are not as comical. I'm the girl who slept with her little Gideon Bible as a security "blanket." And the one who was thankful for Monday night football so I would be asleep before my stepdad went to bed.

For our Grace Maps, we are labeling the teen/young adult years as ages thirteen to twenty. We make many life-impacting decisions during these years. Hormones, acceptance of our peers, growing expectations from others, and feeling equally mature and childlike are interesting combinations for our growing minds and bodies to process.

As our teen years progress to our twenties, we are thrust into the adult world, ready or not. As we move from this season to the next, the pressures of adult responsibilities begin to weigh heavier, and the realization that adulting is hard becomes much clearer. For most of us, scars and promises fill these years.

Did any critical or central events happen during this season (13-20)? (i.e., divorce, deaths, births, salvation, moving, changing schools, friends lost or gained, world events, etc.)

How did you feel about yourself during your teen/young adult years? Include reflections about body image and your intellect.

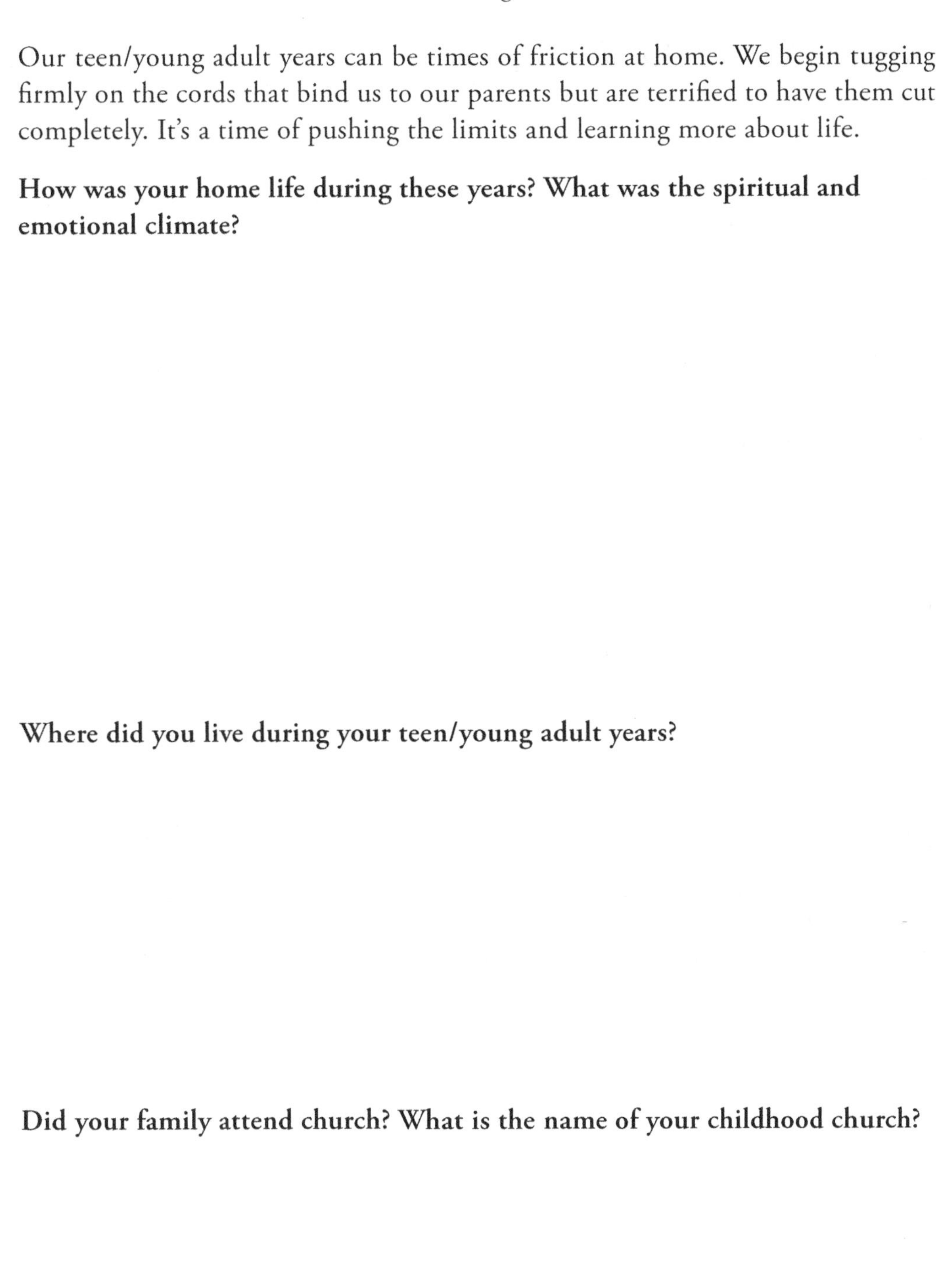

Our teen/young adult years can be times of friction at home. We begin tugging firmly on the cords that bind us to our parents but are terrified to have them cut completely. It's a time of pushing the limits and learning more about life.

How was your home life during these years? What was the spiritual and emotional climate?

Where did you live during your teen/young adult years?

Did your family attend church? What is the name of your childhood church?

Were you a part of a church youth group?

Who made the most impact on you in your home church?

My childhood home church was like family to me. I felt loved and supported. I not only heard about the love of Jesus there, but I also felt His love through their words and actions.

Did you feel loved during this season of life?

I'm a firm believer that we should tell people we love them. Like, out loud, speak it. However, actions also show love. **Realizing this, can you see where some people in your life might have shown love in less verbal ways?**

This question is an important one for me. I found a card I gave momma (when I was a child) that she kept in her treasure box. I had written, "I wish you would hug me." I knew mom loved me, but I wanted more of something a little more tangible as a little girl. As an adult, I see how mom showed me her love in many other less physical ways.

1 Corinthians 13 talks about the way of love. Have you ever read it in The Message translation? Savor every word of verses 1-3:

> "If I speak with human eloquence and angelic ecstasy but don't love, I'm nothing but the creaking of a rusty gate. If I speak God's Word with power, revealing all his mysteries and making everything plain as day, and if I have faith that says to a mountain, 'Jump,' and it jumps, but I don't love, I'm nothing. If I give everything I own to the poor and even go to the stake to be burned as a martyr, but I don't love, I've gotten nowhere. So, no matter what I say, what I believe, and what I do, I'm bankrupt without love."

One of our most life-changing discoveries is the truth of God's love for us. We must take this knowledge from our heads to our hearts. Our belief in His love is integral in making choices that lead to an abundant life.

Draw a line from the reference to the corresponding truth about God's love.

God...

Knows you	John 14:1-3
Planned for you	Romans 5:8
Guides you	Matthew 10:30
Protects you	Psalm 139:16
Died for you	Isaiah 41:10
Will return for you	John 10:27-28

Understanding, as much as our finite minds can, the depth of God's love creates a security that enables us to live without anxiety and fear. I continue on the path of this understanding. But make no mistake, this is a lifelong journey.

Let's continue to mine our memories for landmarks. Remember, you don't have to answer every question. I provide them to prompt your memory.

What schools did you attend?

Who was your favorite teacher?

What was your favorite class?

Were you in extracurricular activities?

Would you consider yourself an insider or outsider at school? Can you explain why you felt that way?

Did you graduate high school?

Did you attend college? If so, where?

If you did not attend college, did you further your education in other ways?

Do you consider yourself adventurous or cautious?

What is the most important life lesson you learned between thirteen and twenty?

Did you have a hobby?

When did you get your first car?

Who was your best friend? What is your fondest memory with this friend?

Who made the most significant positive impact on you during your teens?

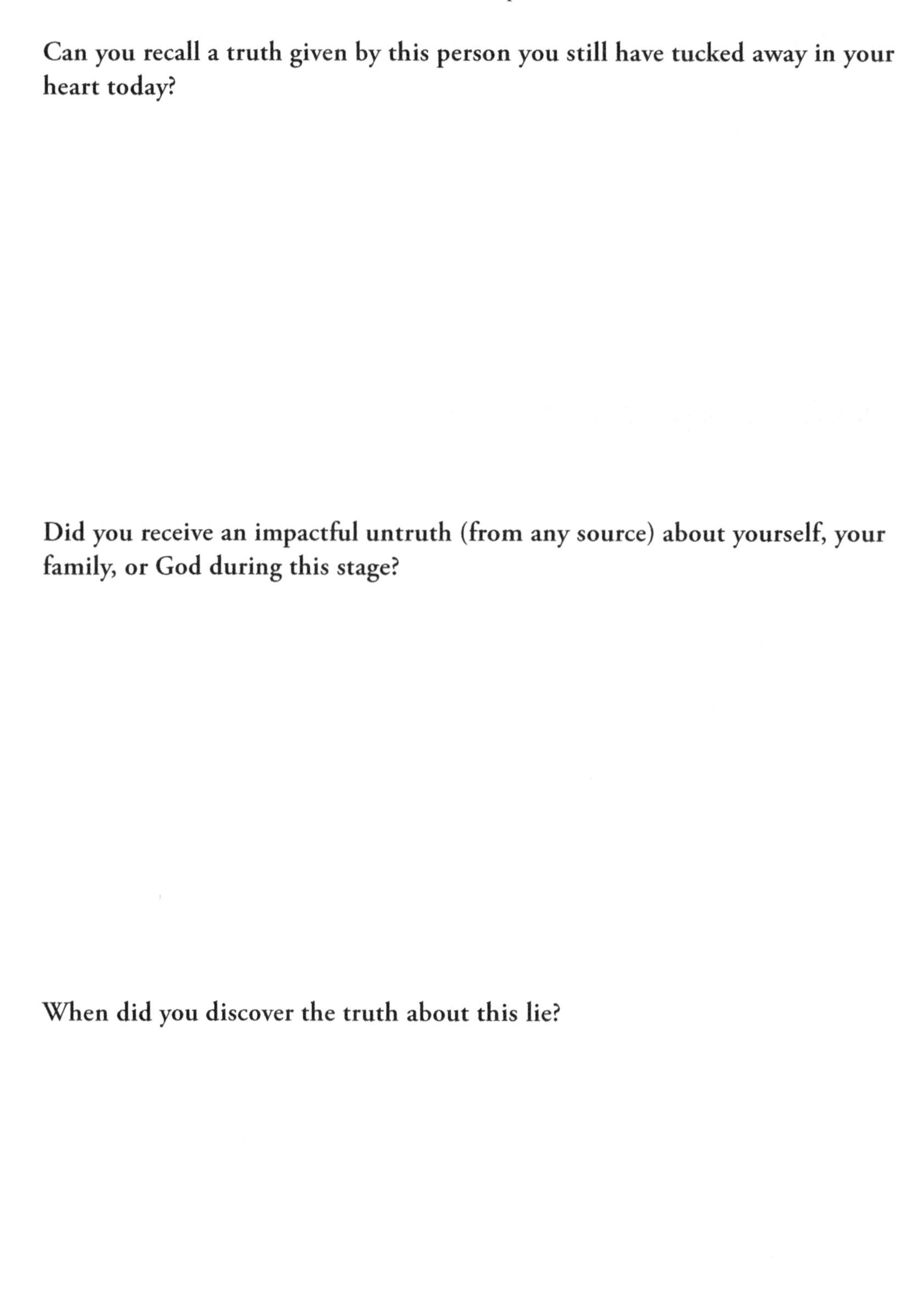

Can you recall a truth given by this person you still have tucked away in your heart today?

Did you receive an impactful untruth (from any source) about yourself, your family, or God during this stage?

When did you discover the truth about this lie?

Do you still struggle with believing this lie? How might God transform your life with this new knowledge if you change your belief about this?

When you think back over this period of your life, can you see God's handiwork?

Do some of the difficult times look different now that you have a few years of hindsight?

Have you been able to help someone else with your teen/young adult testimony?

Time to pause and add some landmarks to your map.

The teen and early adult years are often tumultuous. As we take our first steps of independence, we often stray from the straight and narrow path. Though many of these memories bring feelings and regret, they are also excellent examples of God's love, mercy, and forgiveness. Looking back on these years may be painful, but we will find blessings when we look specifically to see God's hand at work.

Scriptural Affirmation:

I have power from the Holy Spirit to be bold, self-disciplined, and loving. (cf *2 Timothy 1:7)*

"There are far better things ahead
than any we leave behind."

—C. S. Lewis

Use this space to summarize how you now see God working in your life during these years.

Teen to Young Adult

Optional Map Key

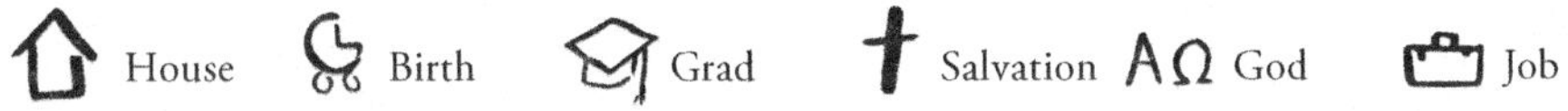

 House  Birth  Grad Salvation AΩ God 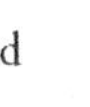 Job

Marriage  School Event  Church  Death  Move

Adult – Twenty One to Forty

"This man's name was Nabal, and his wife, Abigail, was a sensible and beautiful woman. But Nabal…was crude and mean in all his dealings." 1 Samuel 25:3 (NLT)

I wonder if Abigail knew of Nabal's cantankerous disposition before marrying him? Did she even have a choice in her mate selection? Her dad probably thought Nabal was a catch for his daughter. I doubt Abigail felt that way. Her name means "father" {source} of joy. In contrast, Nabal's name means "fool." We can imagine the only respect he enjoyed was the kind his money purchased.

Abigail's story (1 Samuel 25) fits nicely into our third season of life — ages twenty-one to forty. Most of us embark on our careers, marry, and begin our families in this time of life. Some of us are delaying marriage or choosing to live single. Many of us also struggle with unexpected challenges like divorce, infertility, and unfulfilling work experiences. We have made it to adulthood and realize life is not always what we thought it would be, especially regarding relationships.

The first lady of Nabal's home awoke daily in a miserable household. She lived in trying circumstances. The writer of 1 Samuel describes Abigail as wise. She had brains as well as beauty. She was a fantastic negotiator, and her servants loved and respected her.

Abigail loved God and trusted Him to help her. Not only is she a woman we can respect, but we would do well to follow her example of keeping our joy in challenging circumstances.

Let's think back over this time in your life. As you look at these years, I pray that you will see how God walked along with you through the good and bad times.

Answer the questions that will help you add important markers to your Grace Map.

What key events happened during this phase? (i.e., divorce, deaths, births, salvation, moving, illness, changing schools, friends lost or gained, world events, etc.)

How would you describe your relationship with God at this time?

Did you attend church? If you attended church, did you serve in any capacity?

Did your childhood religious beliefs change during this season?

Who made the most profound spiritual impact on you?

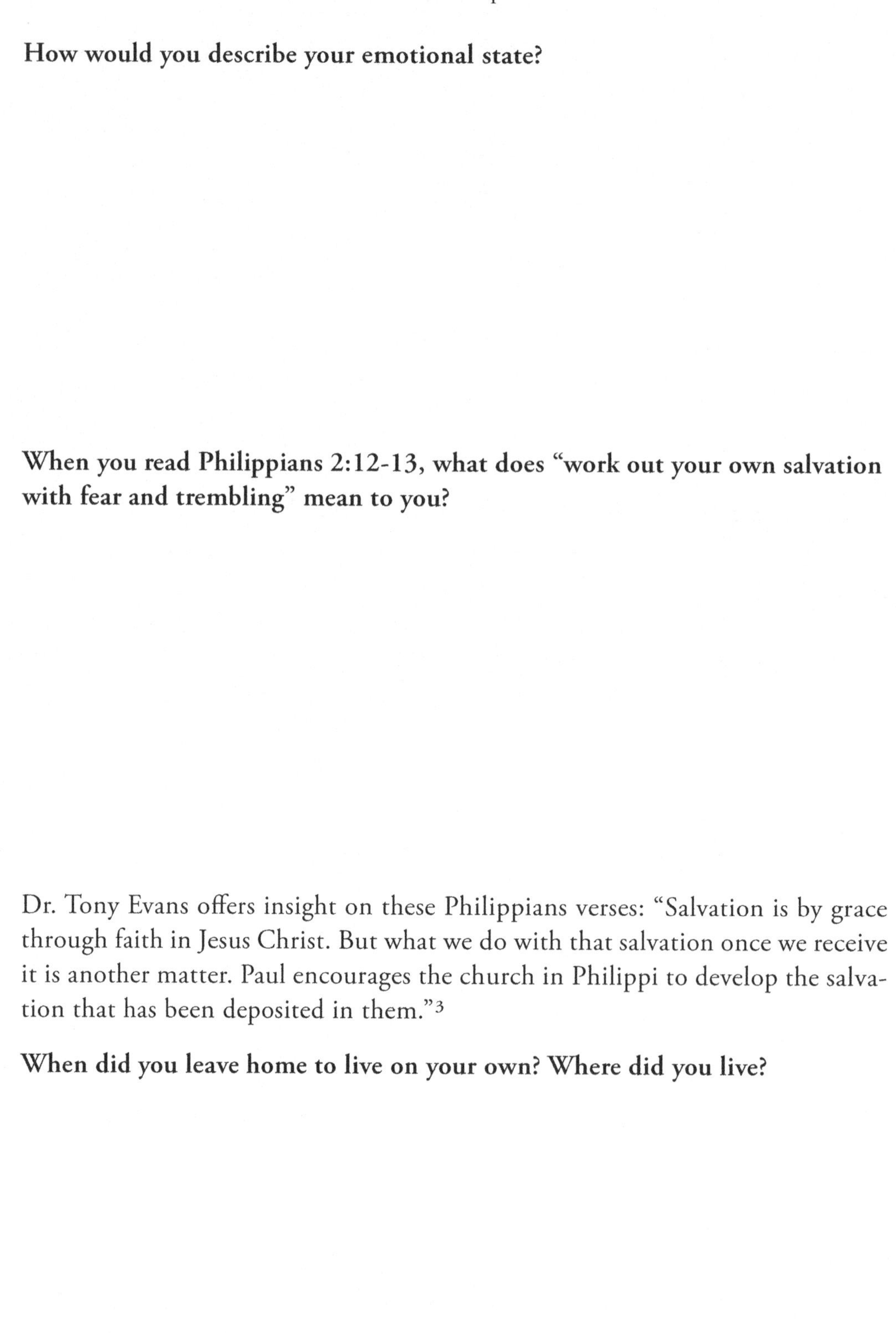

How would you describe your emotional state?

When you read Philippians 2:12-13, what does "work out your own salvation with fear and trembling" mean to you?

Dr. Tony Evans offers insight on these Philippians verses: "Salvation is by grace through faith in Jesus Christ. But what we do with that salvation once we receive it is another matter. Paul encourages the church in Philippi to develop the salvation that has been deposited in them."[3]

When did you leave home to live on your own? Where did you live?

3 Dr. Tony Evans, *The Tony Evans Bible Commentary,* Holman Bible Publishers, 2019, 1241

How did you choose your career, and why?

Were you able to work in your chosen career field?

Were you married or single during this season?

If you were married, how would you describe your marriage?

"Who we are in the present includes
who we were in the past."

– *Fred Rogers*

What marital lessons did you learn during this season?

If you were single, how did you feel about it?

Did you feel judged for not being married?

Are you divorced?

How has your divorce affected you emotionally and financially?

Did you have a support system to help you process the changes divorce brings to you and your family?

Did you have children? If you have children, what are their names?

Whether you were a stay-at-home, work-from-home, or working-outside-the-home mom, how did you feel about this arrangement?

How did you approach being a parent?

Where did you acquire information on parenting?

How would you describe your relationship with your parents?

Who was your best friend?

Did you have hobbies?

Were you able to travel during these years? If so, describe your favorite destination.

Did you have physical health issues? If so, did managing them affect your quality of life?

Several years ago, I was honored to organize a mentoring program at my local church. One of the first decisions I made was not to pair women only using physical age but to attempt (lots of prayers involved doing it this way) to pair women younger in their faith with someone who had walked with God a little longer.

Did you have a mentor?

Have you ever mentored anyone?

Connecting with women, who are a little bit farther along in their spiritual journey, helps us navigate some of our struggles. For example, I might have had a better body image if I had sought a mentor during these years.

I spent so much of my young adult life disliking how I looked. Gosh, I wish I was as overweight now as I was when I thought I was overweight in my younger years. Don't you? My negative body image directed my actions in numerous ways. It robbed me of joy and stopped me from participating in activities. How I thought I looked in a swimsuit dictated my summer plans. I have spent much of my life chained to a scale.

Believing the lie that I was not pretty enough, skinny enough, tan enough, or smart enough stole time from me I cannot regain. These are areas where I still struggle. Bringing up the hot topic of swimsuits in a group of women tells me I'm not alone in my insecurities. Choosing to search for Scripture about our identity in Christ and deposit its truth in our hearts and minds is one way to renew our minds.

Look up Psalm 139:14 and Ephesians 2:10, and write your favorite one below.

Another one of my favorite verses to establish a positive body image is Song of Solomon 4:7 (ESV), "You are altogether beautiful, my love; there is no flaw in you."

Fear of failure may be another pothole we encounter. This fear is a heavy weight to carry. Some of us came from homes where we felt we could never satisfy our parents. We felt like nothing we did was ever good enough. This feeling often affects our decision-making process and our confidence.

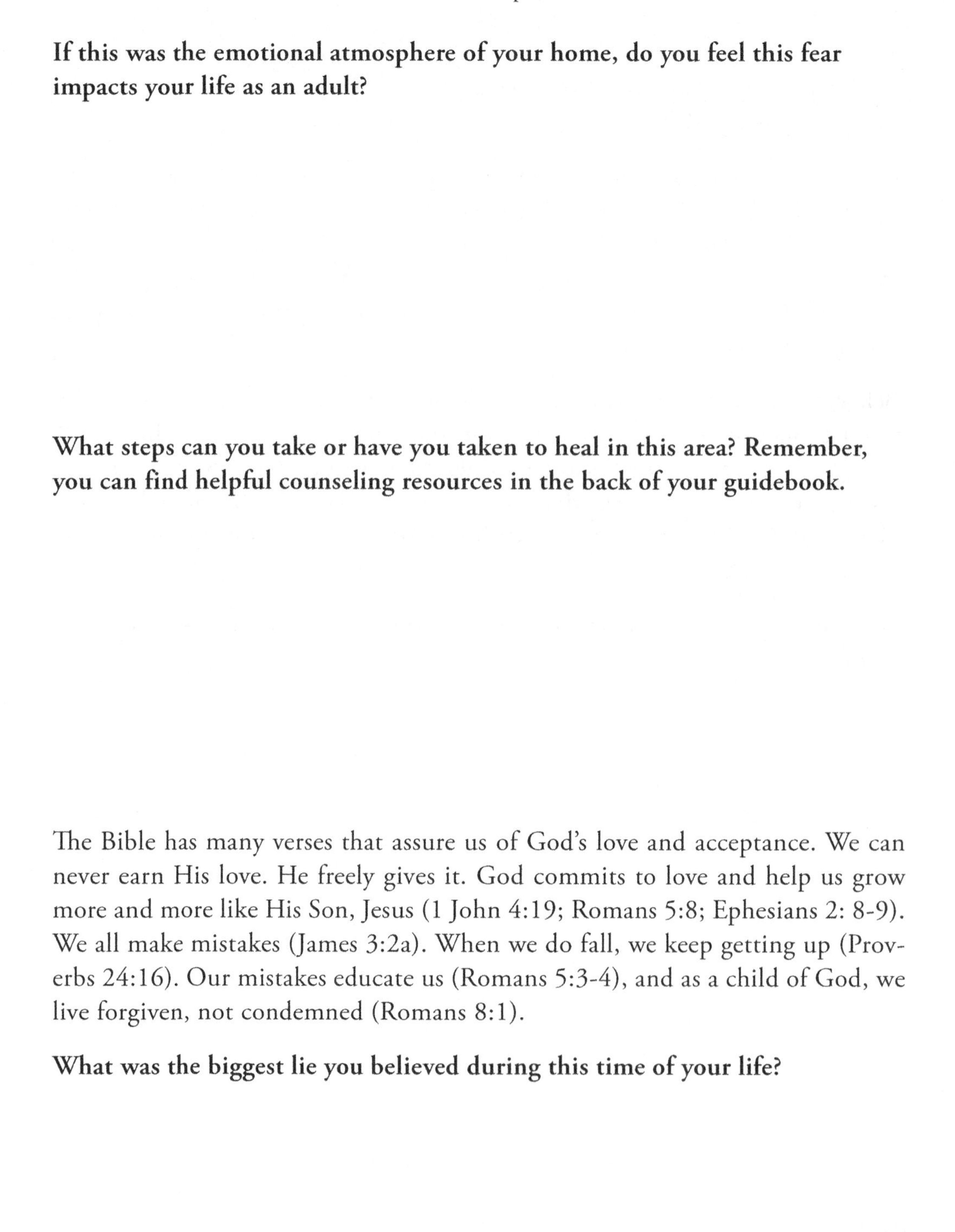

If this was the emotional atmosphere of your home, do you feel this fear impacts your life as an adult?

What steps can you take or have you taken to heal in this area? Remember, you can find helpful counseling resources in the back of your guidebook.

The Bible has many verses that assure us of God's love and acceptance. We can never earn His love. He freely gives it. God commits to love and help us grow more and more like His Son, Jesus (1 John 4:19; Romans 5:8; Ephesians 2: 8-9). We all make mistakes (James 3:2a). When we do fall, we keep getting up (Proverbs 24:16). Our mistakes educate us (Romans 5:3-4), and as a child of God, we live forgiven, not condemned (Romans 8:1).

What was the biggest lie you believed during this time of your life?

When did you learn the truth, and how did it make you feel?

What is your happiest memory during this time?

What is your most difficult memory?

“Isn’t it funny how day by day nothing changes, but when you look back, everything is different?”

—C. S. Lewis

In retrospect, can you see ways God redeemed your difficult memories? If so, how?

How could you describe this differently than you have in the past?

Did you learn any valuable lessons?

Have you been able to help someone else with your testimony?

Time to pause and add some landmarks to your map.

From ages twenty-one to forty, we tend to wrestle with comparison and insecurity. We wonder if who we are and what we're doing is as good as everybody else. We struggle to feel good enough. But when we take a step back and look at these two decades through the lens of God's love for us, we can begin to see how His care and commitment are what makes us worthy.

Scriptural Affirmation:

Death nor life, no one, no thing, and no power can ever separate me from the love of God through Christ Jesus. (cf *Romans 8:38-39)*

Use this space to summarize how you now see God working in your life during these years.

Adult

Optional Map Key

 House  Birth  Grad  Salvation AΩ God  Job

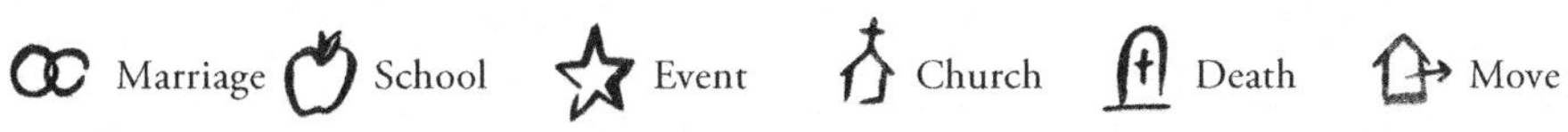

Marriage  School Event  Church  Death  Move

Middle Age – Forty One to Sixty Four

"It has seemed good to me to show the signs and wonders that the Most High God has done for me." Daniel 4:2 (ESV)

When I turned forty, I read that forty was the new twenty. When I celebrated fifty, I learned that fifty was the new thirty. Somehow, for me, fifty didn't always feel like thirty.

I did feel more of a sense of peacefulness and contentment I had lacked in my earlier years. Don't misunderstand. I was not always peaceful and content, but I was beginning to feel much more comfortable with who God made me to be. You kinda start feeling more grown-up in your fifties, right?

Our children (if we have them) are getting a little older and more self-sufficient during these years. We are advancing in our careers if we chose that path. Hopefully, we better understand our God-given gifts and talents and use them to benefit God's Kingdom here on earth.

Most good Christian girls grew up aspiring to be Proverbs 31 Women. The thing about it is, I don't think we understand what it means to be one. Our lack of understanding often makes us feel like a failure. Lydia's story (Acts 16: 11-15, 40) spotlights how that might look in real life.

Lydia was a Gentile by birth who worshipped the God of the Jews. She was a prosperous businesswoman, a merchant of the expensive purple cloth that brought her region of Greece prominence.

When Paul first met Lydia, she was gathering with others outside Philippi for Sabbath prayer.

In the six verses dedicated to Lydia, we learn some great attributes of being a godly woman:

- She gathered with others to worship God. He created us to need community.
- She was faithful in following God with the spiritual knowledge she had and was willing to learn more.
- She listened well and followed God's lead.
- Her conversion was discernible. Because of this, she could tell others her story and lead them to Christ. She started with those in her household.
- She used her resources to help others

When we look at Lydia's life, being a godly woman doesn't seem so unattainable.

Like Lydia, our middle years are fertile ground for growth. But sometimes, it takes intentionality to uncover the good stuff. So, let's look at what happened during this chapter of your life so you can add points of interest to your Grace Map.

What key events happened during this phase? (i.e., marriage, divorce, deaths, births, salvation, moving, illness, friends lost or gained, world events, etc.)

How did you or do you feel about being middle-aged?

What kinds of activities do you consider self-care? Do you make time for them?

Are you caring for your body physically? How?

What do you do for fun?

Are you married or widowed?

If you are widowed, there is no doubt that your husband's loss affects you significantly emotionally, but how has losing him affected your quality of life financially?

If you are single, how do you feel this affects your life?

What positives of the single life have you discovered?

Are you divorced?

How has your divorce affected you emotionally and financially?

Did you have a support system to help you process the changes divorce brings to you and your family?

Do you have grandchildren? What are their names?

How many nieces and nephews do you have? What are their names?

Are your parents still living?

Do you live close to your parents, children, grandchildren, or other family members?

Are you a member of the sandwich generation? Do you financially, physically, or emotionally support your parents and your children?

Where have you lived during this season? Do you remember the addresses?

Do you have hobbies?

Were you able to travel during these years? If so, describe your favorite destination.

Who is your best friend? Or do you have a core tribe of women whose support is mutual?

"Life can only be enjoyed as one acquires a true perspective of life and death and of the real purpose of life."

— Spiros Zodhiates

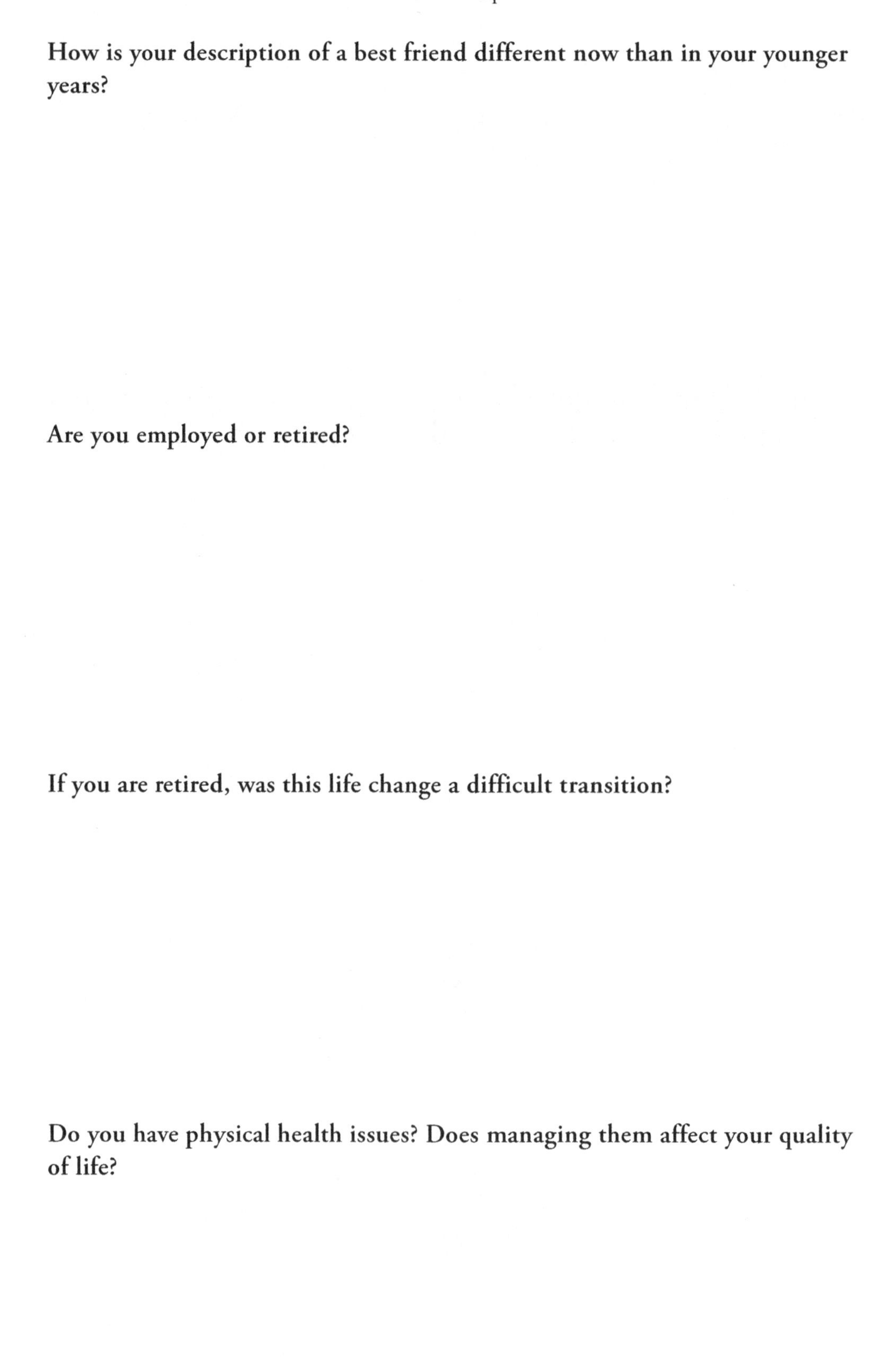

How is your description of a best friend different now than in your younger years?

Are you employed or retired?

If you are retired, was this life change a difficult transition?

Do you have physical health issues? Does managing them affect your quality of life?

What is your biggest blessing?

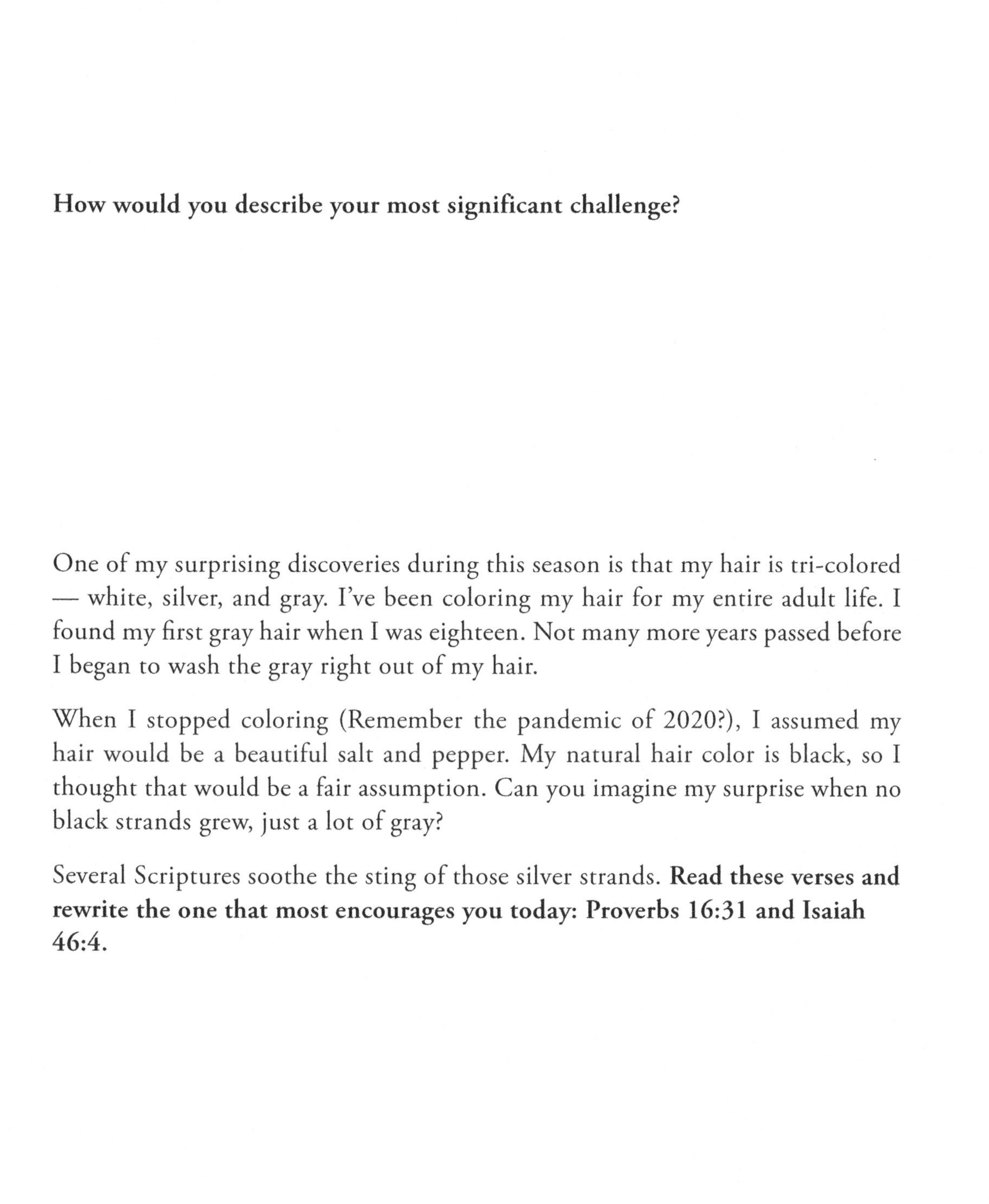

How would you describe your most significant challenge?

One of my surprising discoveries during this season is that my hair is tri-colored — white, silver, and gray. I've been coloring my hair for my entire adult life. I found my first gray hair when I was eighteen. Not many more years passed before I began to wash the gray right out of my hair.

When I stopped coloring (Remember the pandemic of 2020?), I assumed my hair would be a beautiful salt and pepper. My natural hair color is black, so I thought that would be a fair assumption. Can you imagine my surprise when no black strands grew, just a lot of gray?

Several Scriptures soothe the sting of those silver strands. **Read these verses and rewrite the one that most encourages you today: Proverbs 16:31 and Isaiah 46:4.**

These are the years when our bodies change in many ways. Don't even get me started on peri-menopause and menopause. I can say that my body now is not the one I had ten to twelve years ago. Geez, Louise.

There are other changes, too. As we age, we may feel less physically attractive. We can begin to feel less useful and more insignificant. We may ask: Can God still use me in my 60s, 70s, 80s, and beyond?

Psalm 92:14 offers a delightful promise for the godly as we advance in age.
Write it out below and receive this promise.

I still want to produce fruit, don't you? I look at my life now and think, *Girl, you have more years behind you than before you.*

Thinking about this probability can cause sadness and many questions about how we have used our time so far. Can God still use us? What do we have to offer the younger generations? Will I continue to grow spiritually?

Philippians 1:6 answers much of our concerns about growing older and our usefulness to the Kingdom.

> "And I am certain that God, who began the good work within you, will continue his work until it is finally finished on the day when Christ Jesus returns." (NLT)

Y'all, God will continue to grow and use us until He takes us home to live with Him. That's shouting grounds!

Because our children are now grown or almost grown (if we are mothers), we have more time to invest in our emotional and spiritual health. So let's talk a bit about where you are in these areas.

How would you describe your emotional state?

How would you describe your relationship with God?

Have you settled into a spiritual discipline routine? (i.e., prayer, Bible reading, fasting, journaling, honoring the Sabbath, service, etc.)

What has changed your spiritual life the most during this season?

Do you attend church? If you attend church, do you serve in any capacity?

What is your happiest memory during this time?

What is your most difficult memory?

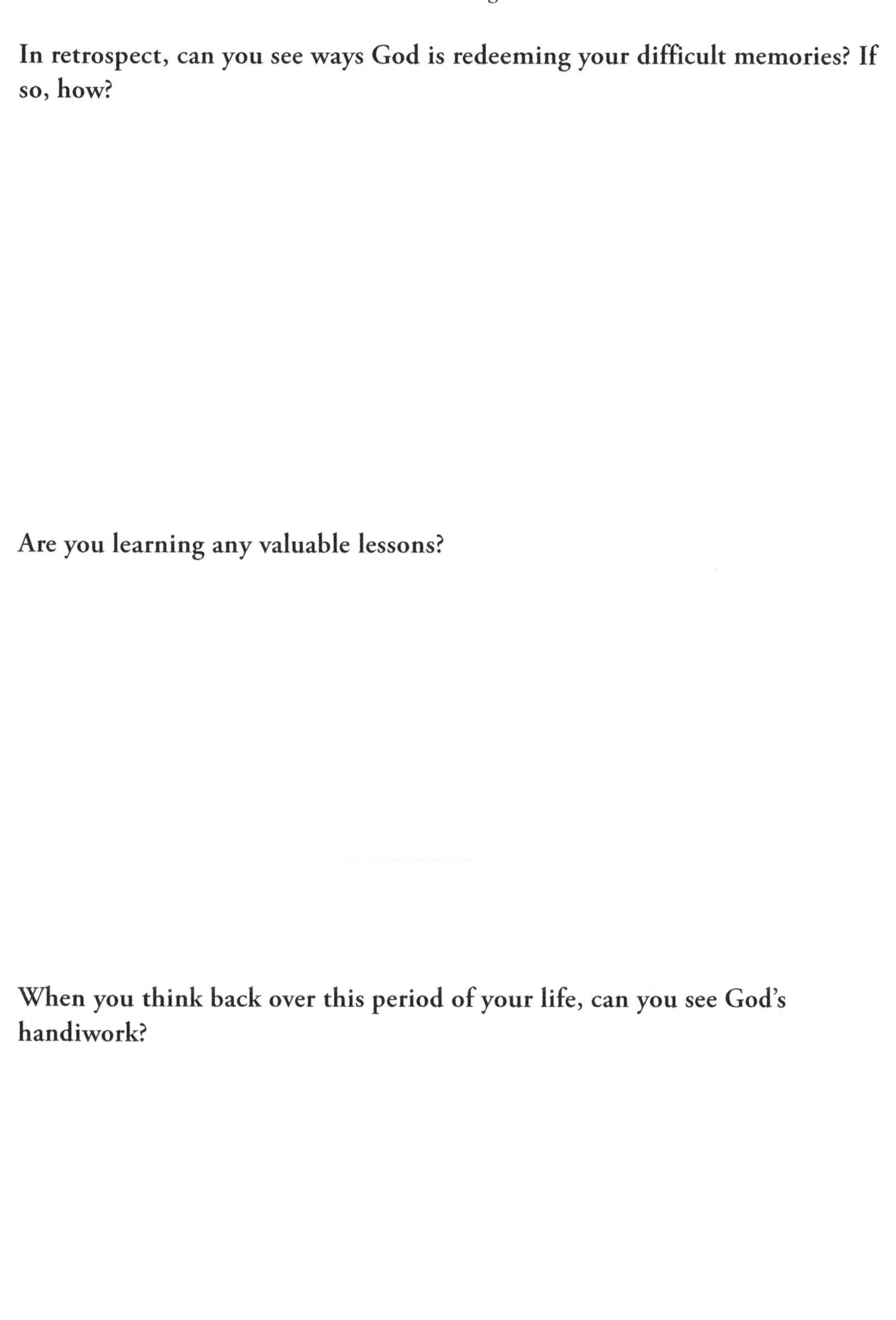

In retrospect, can you see ways God is redeeming your difficult memories? If so, how?

Are you learning any valuable lessons?

When you think back over this period of your life, can you see God's handiwork?

"Life is a song, sing it. Life is a struggle, accept it."

–Mother Teresa

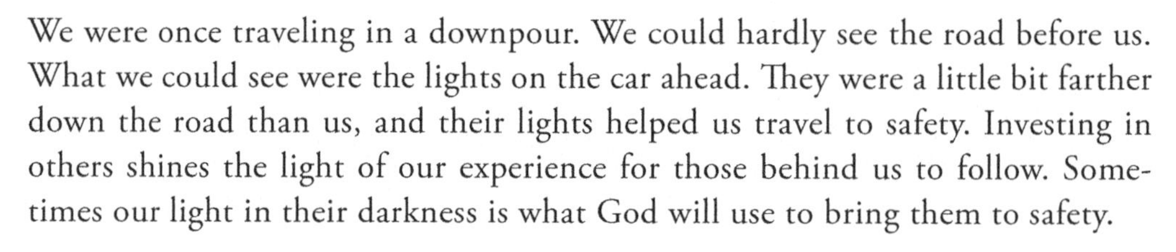

We were once traveling in a downpour. We could hardly see the road before us. What we could see were the lights on the car ahead. They were a little bit farther down the road than us, and their lights helped us travel to safety. Investing in others shines the light of our experience for those behind us to follow. Sometimes our light in their darkness is what God will use to bring them to safety.

Are you investing in the younger generation?

Do you really listen as those younger than you share?

We need each other. What does mutual respect across the generations mean to you?

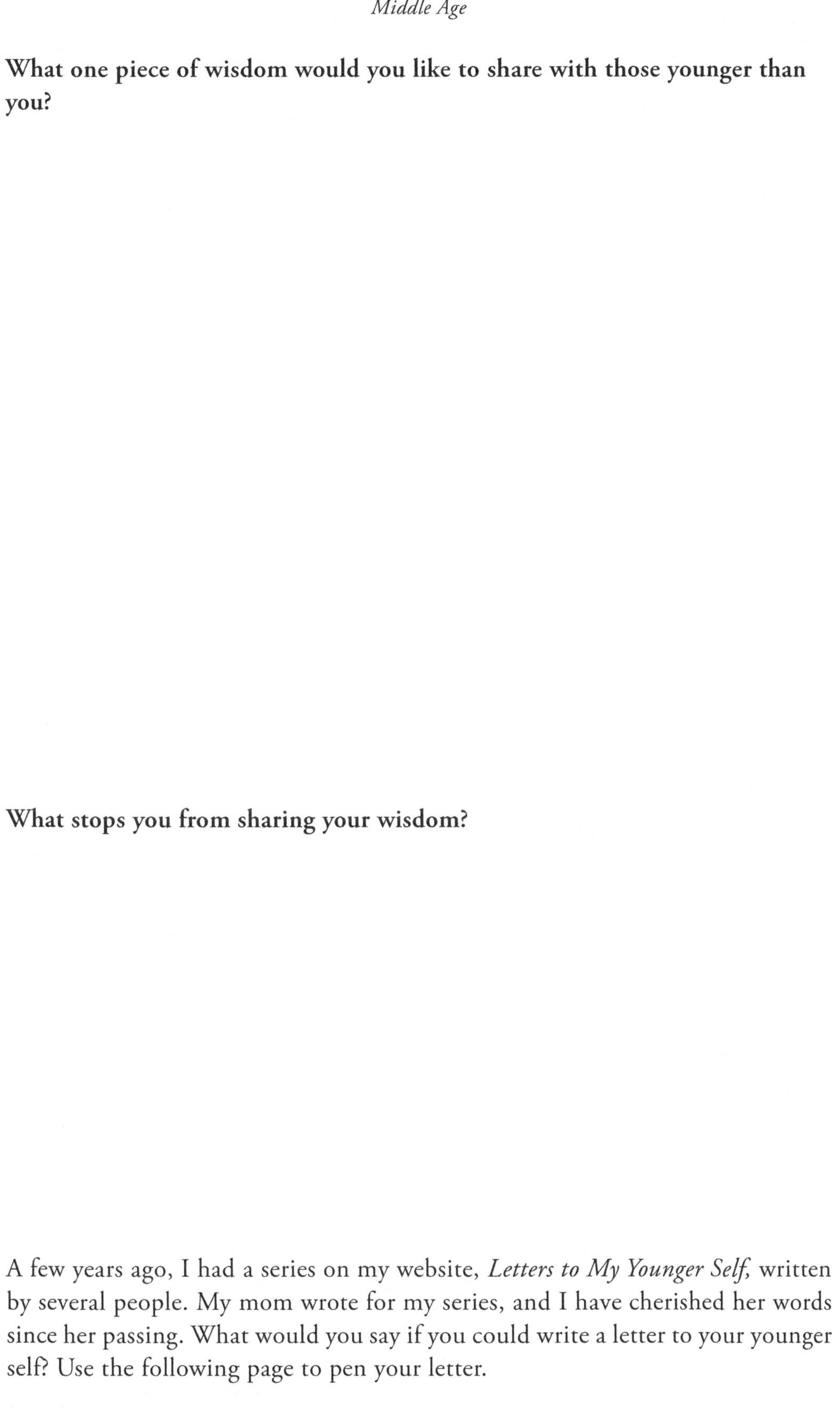

What one piece of wisdom would you like to share with those younger than you?

What stops you from sharing your wisdom?

A few years ago, I had a series on my website, *Letters to My Younger Self,* written by several people. My mom wrote for my series, and I have cherished her words since her passing. What would you say if you could write a letter to your younger self? Use the following page to pen your letter.

From ages forty-one to sixty-five, we face many life changes. Yet, despite all these changes, we also tend to become more content with ourselves and the path God has taken us through in life. If we are open to them, God provides us with opportunities to pass on the lessons we've learned to the next generation. Identifying the markers of God's grace on your Grace Map will help you share His faithfulness along the journey.

Don't forget to add milestones to your Grace Map.

Scriptural Affirmation:

God will finish the good work He began in me long ago. (cf *Philippians 1:6)*

Use this space to summarize how you now see God working in your life during these years.

Middle Age

Optional Map Key

 House Birth  Grad  Salvation AΩ God  Job

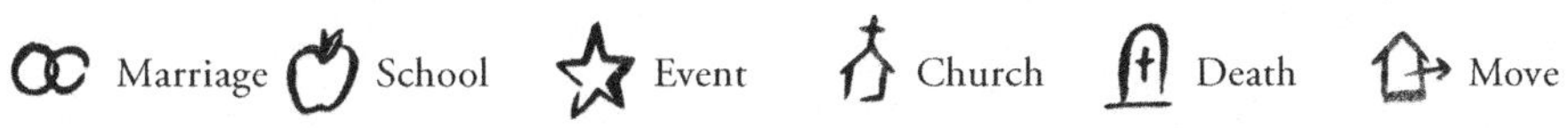

Marriage  School Event Church  Death  Move

"When granted many years of life, growing old in age is natural, but growing old with grace is a choice."

—Rev. Billy Graham

The Golden Years – Sixty Five and Forward

I asked my friend, Betsy,[4] to share her thoughts on her current season. Her gentle fingerprints are found on many of the questions for *The Golden Years,* too.

> "During this stage of life, we feel a new kind of freedom, and yet we realize that our time is limited. What we can do has shifted. It's important to recognize our limitations but focus on what we can do rather than what we can't. Yes, it's sobering to know that our bodies are failing, our minds sometimes struggle, loved ones die, and the world's condition disturbs us. Just remember that all those things happen at any life stage. Keep perspective! Revel in the fact that you are closer to God now than at any other point in your life. You know the power of His love and protection, and you lean into Him for strength and renewal. His promises and hope abound. He is our Rock and inheritance."

4 Betsy Ringer is a speaker, author, and mentor. She offered a treasure trove of beautiful, wise content for the *Golden Years*

Let's assess where you are, how you feel, and what legacy you want to leave behind. If you have not yet reached this stage of life, spend some time contemplating how you would like to be able to answer these questions when you do arrive.

List the places you have lived.

Who are your closest friends?

How would you describe your relationship with God?

Do you attend a local church? What is the name of your congregation?

How do you contribute to your family, church, and community?

What friends and family have died? Who do you miss the most?

How many really good years do you feel you have left?

How do you want to live those years?

How do you feel about getting older?

What are your limitations now?

Maybe you are in a time when you need to receive care. If so, pray for your caregivers. We seem to have more time to pray, study, and offer comfort as we grow older. Don't discount the importance of your prayers and encouragement. You know the old saying, "When you run out of things to pray for, pray for me." You won't waste one prayer. We all need intercession.

What things do you enjoy that you can still participate in?

Make a list of two or three things you would like to learn to do. What will you learn first? When will you start?

It is never too late to learn something new. When my mom lost her hearing completely, she went from talking on her phone to texting. I was concerned. Mom was a free spirit and did not like reading the directions. We went over how to text, and I told her to practice. One day, I received a text from her with a picture. A picture! She wanted to communicate with us, and she decided to learn a new skill.

The feelings we have about getting older can make us feel fearful, hopeless, and filled with anxiety. We may grieve the "what could have beens" in our life. Once we acknowledge those feelings, we can surrender them to God and focus on the gift of each and every day.

If the years sixty-five and forward teach us anything, hopefully, it is that our battles need spiritual weapons. The Apostle Paul teaches us to take our thoughts captive (2 Corinthians 10:5). Cultivating this skill helps us combat negativity by using the Sword of the Spirit — the Word of God (Ephesians 6:17).

Let's look at a few encouraging verses to get us started replacing negative thoughts with the truth of God's Word. This one in The Message assures us that we can continue to grow no matter what is happening with our physical bodies.

> "So we're not giving up. How could we! Even though on the outside it often looks like things are falling apart on us, on the inside, where God is making new life, not a day goes by without his unfolding grace. These hard times are small potatoes compared to the coming good times, the lavish celebration prepared for us. There's far more here than meets the eye. The things we see now are here today, gone tomorrow. But the things we can't see now will last forever." 2 Corinthians 4: 16-18 (MSG)

"He will keep you strong to the end so that you will be free from all blame on the day when our Lord Jesus Christ returns. God will do this, for he is faithful to do what he says, and he has invited you into partnership with his Son, Jesus Christ our Lord." 1 Corinthians 1: 8-9 (NLT)

Take a moment to read and write Isaiah 46:4 and Psalm 73:26. Record the promises God makes to us in these verses.

The Reverend Billy Graham once said, "The greatest legacy one can pass on to one's children and grandchildren is not money, but rather a legacy of character and faith."

Betsy adds, "Pour your encouragement into anyone younger than you. This will give you an opportunity to pass your experience and wisdom on to the generations that follow. Give them a glimpse of how an intimate relationship with God looks. The younger generation needs your knowledge and wisdom. You won't find the word retire in the Bible. Scale down, but don't stop. Find what you are most passionate about and focus on that. Remember, we pass legacy with simple, meaningful actions. Blessing others in small ways is like planting a seed that will one day flower beautifully."

Having a daughter reminds me often of how much each generation needs the other. She helps me see life from a different perspective. We need the thoughts and ideas of those around us. We are not always right, and we don't always have answers. Reach out to someone younger than yourself. Send a handwritten note, gift them a devotional book, invite them to your house to visit, or offer to teach them a skill. Above all, listen. We build relationships best when we feel heard.

Imagine you are turning 80. At your party, each guest describes how you have positively impacted them or something about you they are fond of. **What would you want them to say?**

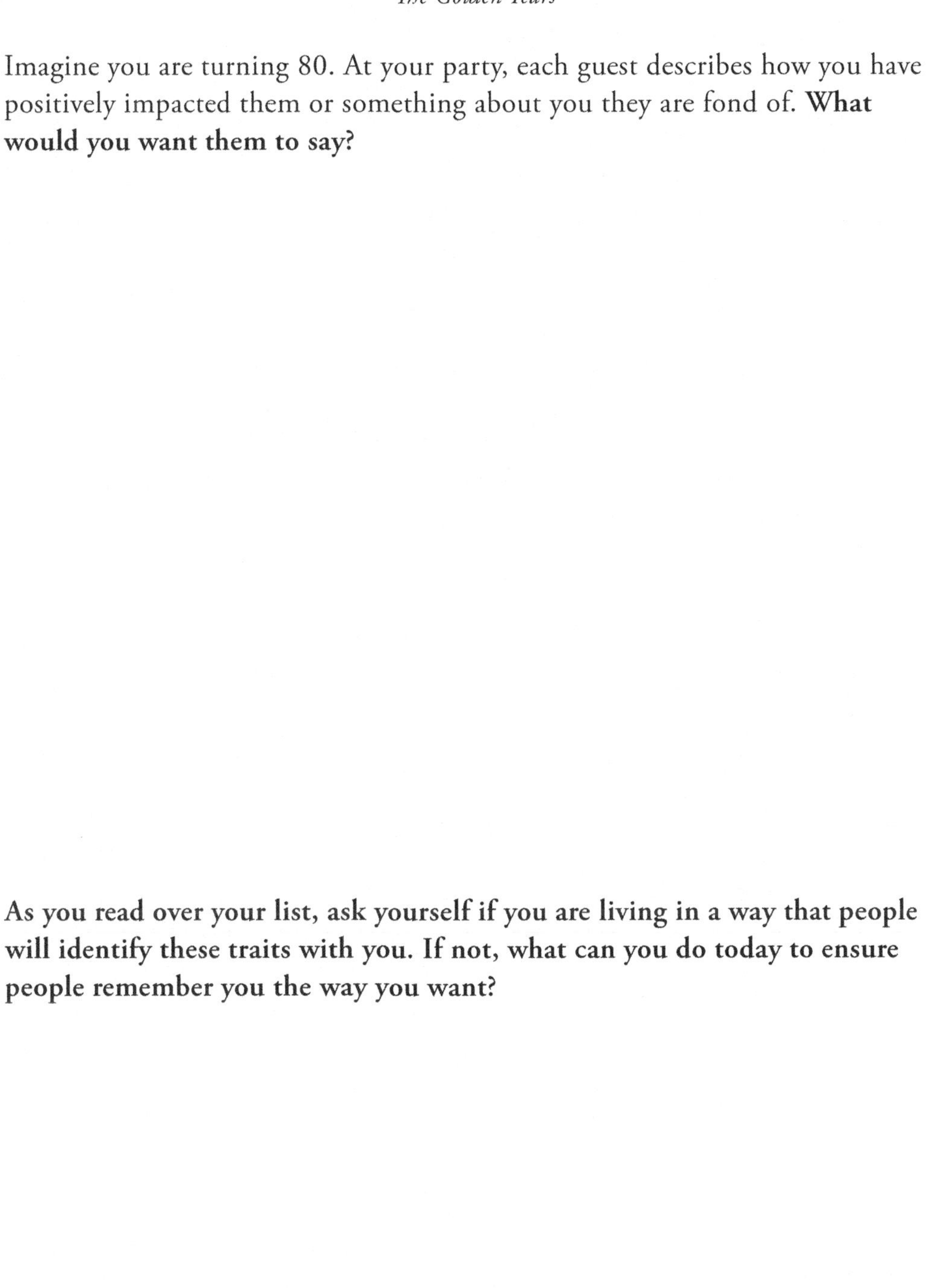

As you read over your list, ask yourself if you are living in a way that people will identify these traits with you. If not, what can you do today to ensure people remember you the way you want?

"Wrinkles should merely indicate where smiles have been."

—Mark Twain

Don't be afraid to plan your own "life celebration." My mom sure did, right down to what color to polish her fingernails — light pink. She picked every song, speaker, and pallbearer. Our family appreciated that she made her wishes known. Grief is complicated, and Mom's plans made our decisions much easier. As I looked over the list she dictated, a few of her song choices were new to me. Good thing she asked me to write them down.

Think back over your spiritual journey. Do you see your spiritual and emotional growth?

What qualities helped you conquer the obstacles that you have faced?

Those same qualities will serve you well as you face future challenges.

We can finish strong, friends.

> "God gives us treasures in life. Partner with God and partner with others to move through this last life stage. Take God's hand and walk into this stage with wisdom and grace. Embrace good health, meaningful activities, and loving relationships. When life throws you a challenge, the investments in relationships and security in God's provision will see you through." — Betsy

LIFE BEYOND

"Don't let your hearts be troubled. Trust in God, and trust also in me." John 14:1 (NLT)

You and I have not personally experienced physical death. However, by this time of life, we have experienced the sting of death for many of our loved ones.

When my mom was diagnosed with advanced cancer, we knew her time would be short. I know she struggled with anxiety and sadness over her prognosis. Yet, she decided early on to set her sights on heaven. She had read Randy Alcorn's book, *Heaven,* a couple of years earlier and was looking forward to meeting Jesus and seeing all the family members who had gone on before her.

Mom's perspective on the most difficult situation she ever faced did not go unnoticed. Her family, especially her children and grandchildren, were given the gift of experiencing a peaceful transition from this world.

How could she be so peaceful in such a devastating time for all of us? Mom had a deep abiding peace in the face of death because she knew God had prepared a perfect place for her. She had walked with Him for many years, trusted Him when her life was in disarray, and believed He loved her. She expected Him to fulfill the promises He made to her and all believers about eternal life.

Here are three verses to hold on to when we fear death: John 3:16, Psalm 23:4, and John 14:1-3. Science proves handwriting helps us to retain what we write. **So choose the one that speaks to your heart and write it below.**

During the last days of her life, my mom felt a presence in the bed with her. She couldn't explain it. She just knew that she felt peaceful and never alone. Was it her guardian angel? Was it the angel that would walk with her as she passed from this life to her final home? I don't know. Her testimony was beautiful and comforting to her and our family. You see, when we die, it is a personal journey. Others may be there to encourage and care for us, but that journey is between our God and us. Knowing she never felt alone was a special gift.

Who was your first really close loved one to pass away?

Do you fear death? What scares you the most?

When he was diagnosed with cancer, my Papaw D said, "I'm not afraid to die, Doll. It's the getting out of here that scares me to death."

Can you relate to his feelings? How so?

I can. I think about papaw's words often. Over and over, the Bible reminds us we don't have to fear death.

> "'O death, where is your victory? O death, where is your sting?' The sting of death is sin, and the power of sin is the law. But thanks be to God, who gives us the victory through our Lord Jesus Christ.'" 1 Corinthians 15:55-57 (ESV)

Dr. Jim Denison wrote, "Imagine a small boy who falls asleep in the back seat of the car. When the family gets home, his father picks him up and carries him into the house. When he wakes up, he's home. That's exactly what happens for us, if Jesus is our Lord."[5]

The Apostle Paul speaks of being absent in our bodies and present with the Lord in 2 Corinthians 5:8. Isn't Dr. Denison's example the sweetest word picture of dying here and opening our eyes to see Jesus?

We will not understand this side of heaven, how dying and death will look for us. We can't know the future, but we can know the One who does. So, if you have never given your heart to Jesus, today is a good day. I have provided a simple salvation prayer to help guide you in the back of our book.

We face many physical losses during the years beyond sixty-five, but we gain an important perspective and an urgency to share our faith in what comes next. As we gain the ability to look back over the entirety of our lives, we see how God weaves together a beautiful map of His grace and faithfulness through decades of twists and turns. Our *Grace Maps* are for His glory! So, how will you share what you've learned with others?

Pause and add waypoints to your Grace Map for this portion of your pilgrimage.

Scriptural Affirmation:

Physical death is not the end for me. My relationship with Jesus Christ assures me of eternal life. (cf *John 11:25*)

5 https://www.denisonforum.org/resources/what-happens-when-we-die/ (April 5, 2021)

Use this space to summarize how you now see God working in your life during these years.

The Golden Years

Optional Map Key

 House  Birth  Grad Salvation AΩ God  Job

Marriage  School Event  Church  Death  Move

A Beautifully Crafted Story

"Come and hear, all you who fear God, and I will tell what he has done for my soul." Psalm 66:16 (ESV)

When Ruth and Naomi arrived in Bethlehem, their journey wasn't over. They had a whole lotta livin' left to do. Ruth needed to meet and marry Boaz so she could bear his son, Obed, who would become King David's grandpa.

Naomi felt like her life had ended in Moab. These are the words she shared with her old friends:

> "'Don't call me Naomi,' she responded. 'Instead call me Mara, for the Almighty has made life very bitter for me. I went away full, but the Lord has brought me home empty. Why call me Naomi when the Lord has caused me to suffer and the Almighty has sent such tragedy upon me?'" Ruth 1:20-21 (NLT)

Naomi's pain was intense. She could not see a path to joy. We know now what Naomi didn't know then; she would indeed begin again during the darkest days of her life. Their return to Bethlehem opened doors with incredible eternal significance. Naomi would one day soon bounce the grandpa of a future king on her knee — an anointed king that would be the predecessor of our King of Kings and Lord of Lords, Jesus Christ.

We don't know how our story will end, either. Even through bitter heartbreak, Naomi had another chapter in her life story. As long as we are on this side of heaven, we will continue to walk out good and bad times.

As we look back over our beautiful *Grace Maps*, we see all those seemingly unrelated times were parts of an astonishing story — a beautifully crafted story that belongs to each of us personally. My story. Your story.

Take notice of the valuable lessons you are learning. I hope you smile as you see God's hands guiding you along your path.

In Habakkuk 2:2, God tells us to "write down the vision and make it plain" so that all who read it may run. I believe part of the vision we need to write down is our testimony to the goodness of God in our lives.

Our paths forward make way for those who travel behind us. Your Grace Map is a lovely visual of God's love and care for you — a visual you can share with whomever you choose. It is a treasured legacy to leave behind.

If you are interested in a beautifully designed map template to create your personal Grace Map, you will find a free one on Carmen's book page, www.gracemapsbook.com

Rejoice, my friend! You did it! You retraced your steps and placed stones of remembrance along the way.

Simple Salvation Prayer

ABCs of Salvation:

A – Admit you have sinned. "For everyone has sinned; we all fall short of God's glorious standard." Romans 3:23 (NLT)

B – Believe in Jesus. "For this is how God loved the world: He gave his one and only Son, so that everyone who believes in him will not perish but have eternal life." John 3:16 (NLT)

C – Confess and leave your sin behind. "But if we confess our sins to him, he is faithful and just to forgive us our sins and to cleanse us from all wickedness." 1 John 1:9 (NLT)

Lord, I admit that I have done wrong things. Thank You that You died to take away all my sins and rose in victory to give me life abundantly. Please forgive me. I receive Your forgiveness now and declare that I want to live for You for the rest of my life. Come and fill me with Your Holy Spirit. I now depend completely on You. In the mighty name of Jesus. Amen.

Welcome to the family of God! Your next steps are:

1. Tell somebody how God changed your life.

2. Begin reading your Bible. The book of John, in the New Testament, is a great place to start.

3. Pray daily. You don't need fancy words. Prayer is talking to God.

4. Find a biblically-sound, local congregation to grow and serve God with the gifts and talents He gave you. If you don't know of one, ask a Christian friend.

If you prayed this prayer for salvation, I would love for you to drop me a note at carmen@carmenhorne.com so I can rejoice with you!

Notes

Notes

Notes

Notes

Notes

Notes

Meet the Author

Carmen Horne is a board-certified Advanced Christian Life Coach for women, author, and speaker who uses her gifts to encourage women. Carmen is passionate about supporting women through life's challenges as they learn to embrace, with hope, the unexpected.

Healing her own damaged heart taught her the hope she now offers to the brokenhearted. Likewise, plowing through unhealthy thinking in her own life shaped Carmen's understanding of the power of perspective. The early seeds of her ministry began with mentoring, lay counseling, and listening ears. Carmen continues to use those tools to offer encouragement.

Carmen is the author of *Out of Words: 31 Prayers of Hope for Your Hurting Heart,* a contributor to *101 Secrets to a Happy Marriage* — Thomas Nelson Publishers, Sweet to the Soul Ministries', *Faith* Magazine, *Warrior Devotional* — Declare Conference, WEGOM's, *The Message* Magazine, *Just Between Us* Magazine, and many online websites and blogs.

At the ripe old age of sixteen, the Bayou State native married her high-school sweetheart, and they consider their beautiful daughter their biggest blessing. Carmen is a dark chocolate nibbler and a beach sitter. But her favorite activities are those she participates in as a wife and mom.

Connect with Carmen on her website at www.carmenhorne.com.

Acknowledgments

Always and foremost, I am deeply grateful for my relationship with Jesus Christ, my Savior. Thank You, Jesus, for saving me, healing me, guiding me, and using me to be Your hands and feet. Your willingness to use this scared, insecure girl as an instrument of peace and encouragement amazes me still. I am humbled to tears at the very thought of it. My heart forever belongs to You, Lord.

Lary and Madison, y'all are always my biggest cheerleaders, always supportive, always assuring me of your love. I love you both big time. I am a blessed woman, indeed. Thank you.

Ellen Chauvin and Stephanie Adams listen to me, discuss life with me, pray with and for me, and ponder the ins and outs of writing. Our morning Voxer gatherings to discuss spiritual nuggets we have unearthed in our quiet times are some of my favorite moments of the day. We cry together, laugh together, and whine together. I often say we have a mastermind group. Not because we are brilliant, but because we have minds, and we chose to surrender them to our Master. Thank you, friends. I think we are better writers and stronger Christians because we are connected. Love you, ladies.

To my Beta Group: Betsy R., Debbie C., Ellen C., Karen S., Kim S., Lucinda D., Nancy B., Sherry M., Stephanie A., Sharlene A., Shelley O., Tammy L., Tyanne R., Veronica S.: Thank you again for walking with me through the journey of *Grace Maps*. The refining tool of your input is invaluable. Your sacrifice of time is most appreciated. Y'all will certainly receive spiritual rewards for the investment you have made into each reader.

Ministry Coach and Project Planner, Christa Hutchins, you are one fantastic book coach. Thank you for your calming influence when I was ready to run away and for sharing your God-given planning and organizational gifts to keep me on track. You are always supportive and compassionate as you encourage me to be my best. I consider you a dear friend.

Taryn Nergaard's team at Typewriter Creative Co. Oh my goodness, you ladies are a joy to work alongside. Taryn and Cassidy, thank you so much for listening to my heart and helping Grace Maps be just as beautiful as I knew she could be. Cassidy is a saint to sort out all those voice messages and find the perfect look for Grace Map's cover. Sara, your work is not as visible as the other team members, but so very vital for Grace Map's success. The information on wording, categories, ad copy, and all things that the booksellers' will need is invaluable. Thank you so much, team!

Editor Liz Giertz, your input is the secret sauce to all of my words. You keep me on brand, calm me down when I realize I'm not and will need to do essential rewrites, and pray me through wonky manuscript reformatting EACH time we swapped edits. Here is a great quote from you to me, "God's got this. Don't freak out." My friend, thank you.

Ministry Collaborative, *His Girls Gather,* thank you for teaching me, encouraging me, laughing with me, and nudging me to step out further into my calling. My attendance at the She Speaks conference in 2015 opened the door for me to be a part of this group, and I will forever be thankful. Love you, ladies!

You may be wondering if you would benefit from the services of a counselor. Here are a few questions to ask yourself as you sort out your feelings on the subject. This list is not exhaustive, and I am not a professional in this field. Please seek professional help if you can answer yes to any of these:

- Has something traumatic happened to you and your pain is still intense and life-altering?
- Are you dealing with grief? Have you lost a loved one, your job, your health, or a dream you had for your life and struggle to move forward?
- Are you depressed? Do you feel sad most of the time and have little hope of things improving? I'm not talking about having the blues. I'm talking about clinical depression.

If you need a counselor, your local church is a great resource to begin searching for a godly one. Many churches offer these services to their members. Here are a few more resources to help you work through dark times:

Grief Share: https://www.griefshare.org/

American Association of Christian Counselors: https://www.aacc.net

Focus on the Family Mental Health Resources:
https://www.focusonthefamily.com/get-help/mental-health-resources/

Faithful Counseling: https://www.faithfulcounseling.com/
Online professional mental health counseling from a biblical perspective.

Carmen's Other Books

Out of Words: 31 Prayers of Hope for Your Hurting Heart

How do you pray with a shattered heart?

Healing feels impossible when our hearts are so shattered words fail us. We cannot pray when the pain is so great; we long for gentle guidance and profound wisdom to guide us as we journey back to trust.

In Carmen's book, *Out of Words: 31 Prayers of Hope for Your Hurting Heart,* she brings the experience and hope we need to regain strength — and find our words. Rooted in Scripture and filled with guidance and clarity from her hard-earned healing, *Out of Words* offers 31 days of insight, specifically crafted prayers, and journal space for you to:

- Discover, or rediscover, the beauty and power of praying God's Word
- Receive comfort as your tender heart heals
- Unpack your devastation to gradually reveal the strength and words you need to recover.

As you process each day with questions from your Hope Coach and journal your thoughts with a Pray and Ponder opportunity, you will rediscover the words to ask God to tenderly care for and heal your broken heart.

For more information on, *Out of Words,* and other book-related resources, visit www.carmenhorne.com/outofwordsbook

Finding Words: Writing from Hurt to Hope

Did you have a diary as a child?

Mine is pink with a fairy-sized padlock. The key has long been lost. I still keep it tucked away in the bottom of a drawer. After 50+ years, I still guard its secrets.

Journals are the keepers of our thoughts and feelings. Writing is a beautiful healing experience. Our fingers are our scribes. Taking pen to paper helps us gain an understanding of our experiences. We take note of our feelings as we pour our grief and painful emotions as freely as the ink flows from the pen.

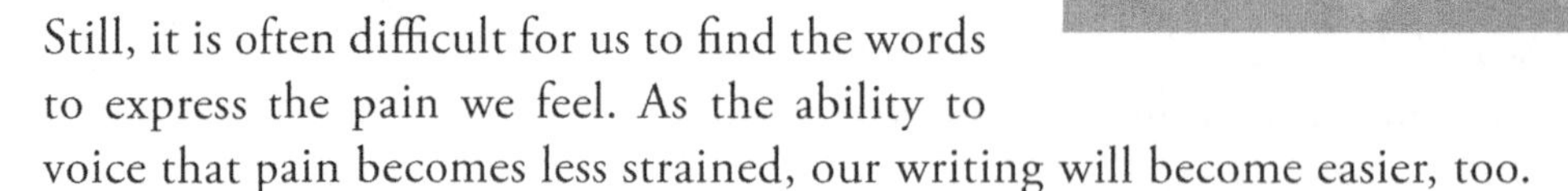

Still, it is often difficult for us to find the words to express the pain we feel. As the ability to voice that pain becomes less strained, our writing will become easier, too.

Releasing feelings through writing is a healthy step toward healing.

In *Finding Words,* the companion journal to her book, *Out of Words,* Carmen provides space to journal your thoughts and prayers. Carefully selected Scriptures, mirroring those referenced in her book, provide comfort and guidance as you continue your healing journey.

Savor this time with your thoughts and with God. He longs to deepen His relationship with you.

"Because he bends down to listen, I will pray as long as I have breath!" Psalm 116:2 (NLT)

For more information on, *Out of Words, Finding Words,* and other resources related to these books, visit www.carmenhorne.com/outofwordsbook

Made in the USA
Monee, IL
16 November 2022

17900932R00090